Soule

GC
57
.S625

Ocean adventure

The Ocean Adventure

THE OCEAN ADVENTURE

SCIENCE EXPLORES
THE DEPTHS OF THE SEA

by Gardner Soule

APPLETON-CENTURY

New York

For Marjorie and

Mark Hopkins (Bill) Barnes

First edition

APPLETON-CENTURY
AFFILIATE OF
MEREDITH PRESS

Library of Congress Catalog Card Number: 66-14956

Acknowledgments

The author wishes to express his thanks to the persons and publishers listed below for their kind cooperation in granting permission to reprint excerpts from copyrighted material.

From *The Galathea Deep Sea Expedition,* by Anton Frederic Bruun, Svend Bernhard Greve, Hakon Mielche, and Hakon Ragnar G. Sparck. Translated by Reginald Spink. Published by George Allen & Unwin Ltd. and used with permission of the publisher.

From a dispatch by Frank Carey distributed by The Associated Press. Used with permission of The Associated Press.

From *Abyss,* by C. P. Idyll. Copyright © 1964 by C. P. Idyll. Thomas Y. Crowell Company, New York, publishers. Reprinted by permission of the publishers.

From *Half Mile Down,* by William Beebe. Copyright 1934, 1951, by William Beebe. Published by Duell, Sloan and Pearce and used with permission of the publisher.

From an article by H. D. Hess appearing in the August, 1965, issue of *Engineering and Mining Journal,* a McGraw-Hill mining publication. Used by permission of the publisher.

From pp. 116–118, 120, 180–181 *The Living Sea,* by Captain J. Y. Cousteau with James Dugan. Copyright © 1963 by Harper

& Row, Publishers, Incorporated. Reprinted by permission of the publishers.

From *The Search Beneath the Sea,* by J. L. B. Smith. Copyright © 1956 by Holt, Rinehart and Winston, Inc. Reprinted by permission of Holt, Rinehart and Winston, Inc.

From *Surface at the Pole,* by Commander James Calvert, U.S.N. Copyright © 1960 by James Calvert. McGraw-Hill Book Company, New York, used by permission of the publisher.

From *"Nautilus" 90 North,* by Commander William R. Anderson, with Clay Blair, Jr. Copyright © 1959 by William R. Anderson and Clay Blair, Jr. Reprinted by permission of The World Publishing Company.

From *Around the World Submerged,* by Captain Edward L. Beach, USN. Reprinted by permission of Holt, Rinehart and Winston, Inc.

Contents

Illustrations

Who hath desired the Sea?—the sight of salt water unbounded—
The heave and the halt and the hurl and the crash of the comber wind-hounded?

—RUDYARD KIPLING

PART I

Man Enters the Depths

The First Round Trips
to Davy Jones's Locker

WHAT IS HAPPENING today in the depths of the sea could not, in all history, ever have happened before:

An American submarine, the *Alvin,* carries her crew to the bottom of the Atlantic, over a mile down. Through ports, her two men stare at a shadowy, boulder-filled sea floor. A second American submarine, the *Aluminaut,* goes even deeper.

Two men, Jon Lindbergh and Robert Stenuit, roam and work on the sea floor at a depth of 432 feet. Stenuit's fingers turn numb as he tries to take pictures. Sardines and shrimp swarm around the divers. Stenuit pets a big fish—a 200-pound grouper. His photo flashes attract six others that jostle him. He looks overhead at king mackerels, jacks, and barracudas, "all twisting and turning tirelessly." Lindbergh and Stenuit remain there 49 hours, but are in no way harmed by the longest deep dive by individual divers on record.

The *Alvin,* the *Aluminaut, Deep Jeep,* and Lindbergh all join in a search off Spain for an accidentally dropped, unexplodable nuclear bomb—the first search ever by the world's first deep-diving fleet. The H-bomb is found and brought up.

Bathyscaphes, in which men make the deepest dives of all, having descended well over six miles in 1960, continue to probe, one after another, some of the deepest trenches under both the Atlantic and the Pacific. Their men find fish at the utmost depths.

A diving saucer makes 125 trips, keeping to a schedule almost as routine as that of a ferryboat, and carries scientists 1,000 feet beneath the surface of the Pacific. On the bottom, they find canyons with overhanging cliffs; octopuses churning up dust clouds out of silt; rare fish caught only once or twice before.

Men in metal houses and workshops live on the bottom of the sea beneath two to three hundred feet or more of salt water for days or weeks at a time. They are able to leave their protecting shelters at will and work on the sea floor.

All of these developments add up to one big development: Man is at last moving into the depths.

Our era has been called the age of petroleum, the age of chemistry, the age of the atom, the age of space. It is all of these things and more.

Our time may also be called the age of the sea. The age of man in the sea is beginning.

The way is now open to the bottom of the sea, any bottom, no matter how deep. Man for the first time in history can go to Davy Jones's locker—and come back alive.

Why? Why should we? Why is man entering the depths from which he has been barred throughout his time on earth?

Eyewitnesses in the depths of the sea will finally behold with their own eyes all that is there. There will be a lot to see. The depths are unexplored. Of course anyone can stand on the edge of a beach and face the sea and see a lot of it, fifteen or twenty miles to the horizon. You can smell the sea, you can feel it, you can taste it. You can swim in the sea and dive into it—down to eighty feet or so if you are a pearl diver, to two or three hundred feet or even more if you are a champion scuba diver. You can learn how salt the sea is, and how cold, and how its buoyancy helps keep you afloat and how it can drown you. You can sail the oceans in ships, as men have been doing at least as long as they have been writing down their history, and possibly much longer; you can get to know the ocean's hurricanes and its calm days and its average (rough) days.

But what is beneath the surface remains a mystery. You can drop your fishing lines and nets and trawls and catch some of the fish in the ocean; but the waters of the sea hide the fish and the other animals and the plants that are beneath it, and even the best fisherman pulls up only a few random samples. But an eyewitness in deep water can see the fish that are there, just as one can see them in shallow water; he can see how they behave, and what other creatures—perhaps unknown monsters—are to be encountered.

Ichthyologists, or fish scientists, as eyewitnesses need to determine whether, as some suppose, the food resources of the depths are more plentiful than the food resources of the continental shelves. Most of today's great fisheries for cod, herring, and other dining-table staples are located on or above the shelves.

In the depths, eyewitness geographers and geologists will explore the world's most spectacular features.

Today's research ships measure the depth of the ocean the modern way by making a sound in the water and listening for its echo to return from the bottom. Echo sounding locates and draws profiles of submarine canyons, mountains, and plains. Echo sounding already has charted the biggest single feature of the whole earth: the great undersea ridge of mountains that runs 10,000 miles down the Atlantic, from Greenland to the Antarctic, then branches out into all the other oceans, making a vast mountain range 45,000 miles long, almost girdling the globe. Echo sounding already has charted an undersea series of canyons, some of them wider, longer, and deeper than the Grand Canyon. Both the suboceanic mountain range and the oceanic series of canyons were sounded by the men around Maurice Ewing, Columbia University's oceanographer. The latest echo sounding reaches down far enough to plumb the depths of the greatest of all gashes in the face of the earth, the deep trenches beneath the sea. On November 6, 1962, the Royal Navy's research vessel, H.M.S. *Cook,* captained by Commander F. W. Hunt, charted a new deepest point in the world's oceans. East of the Philippines in the Mindanao Trench, a depth of 37,782 feet or over 7 miles was found. The Cook Deep, as it has been named, could hold Mount Everest, at 29,028 feet the world's tallest mountain, and there would still be room to add seven Empire State Buildings, stacked one upon the other, above the summit. Men today can haul up samples of rocks and sediments even from the deepest trenches.

Eyewitnesses are still needed in the depths. Geologists need to explore the undersea mountains and canyons and trenches and study for themselves their rocks and formations. A new field of activity is opening: undersea mountaineering.

Because in the past he has not been able to explore the depths as an eyewitness, man's information about them has, up to now, been fragmentary. Four centuries before Christ, Alexander the Great apparently took a peep beneath the sea. He may have had a look at the bottom 20 or 30 feet below the surface in some kind of diving bell. Even today, it is difficult for a diver to go below 300 feet, and how to stay down for more than a matter of minutes is just being learned by Jon Lindbergh and other divers. So most clues about the depths have come from what is dredged or trawled up: rocks, sediment, animals. For centuries men supposed no life existed in the depths. In the years 1817–19 John Ross dredged up worms and a starfish from 6,000 feet down. In 1860 G. C. Wallich, an American geologist, concluded that life would be found many miles below the surface in the deepest abysses. Not till 1951 (Chapter 20) and 1960 (Chapter 21) was the proof obtained that Wallich was right. Meantime, as oceanography developed, the evidence in Wallich's favor was growing. In 1860 a cable raised from 7,000 feet down in the Mediterranean brought up animals: coral, oysters, snails, scallops, squid eggs. Then the great breakthrough in the development of oceanography as a science came from the *Challenger* expedition. In 1872 Britain sent out a three-masted corvette, the *Challenger,* to explore the seas. She made a 3½-year cruise, brought up animals, took water samples, took soundings, mapped currents, sampled the bottom. An American, Alexander Agassiz, who contributed two volumes to the *Challenger* reports, was first to use steel cables for deep-sea dredging. He invented a trawl that was more efficient and a fine net to sample at different depths the plankton, or microscopic animal and plant life in the sea. As long ago as 1882 the United States built its first oceanographic vessel, the *Albatross*. In time she took more soundings, mapped more sea floor, and hauled up more deep-sea fishes than had the *Challenger*. France, Russia, Belgium, Italy, and Germany in the late nineteenth century sent out their own oceanographic vessels. Prince Albert I of Monaco studied currents, the sea floor, whales, and giant squid, and founded the Oceanographic Museum in Monaco in 1910.

Along with our new fleet of deep-diving vessels, surface ships like *Challenger* and *Albatross* continue probing the depths. Today's include the new *Atlantis II* of the Woods Hole Oceanographic Institution and the old schooner *Vema* of Columbia University's Lamont Geological Observatory; Maurice Ewing, an oceanographer, has spent more time aboard *Vema* than in any home in which he has ever lived. Sailing vessels have been better for oceanographic research than steamships. Using the wind for power, schooners can stay out for weeks or months at a time to observe winds, waves, currents, and weather, whereas steamships have to come into port often to refuel. Power now is replacing sail.

Woods Hole, Lamont, the Scripps Institution of Oceanography, and others make of oceanography today a full-time, year-round business, not just an occasional expedition as in the days of the *Challenger*. This will make all the difference in the world. It will mean eventually that our information about the depths will no longer be fragmentary. New knowledge is coming in from the sea in a steady flow these days, and a far more complete picture of the depths than man ever had before is being put together. On a full-time basis—that is how science is exploring the depths today.

Eyewitnesses can also better locate the mineral wealth known to be in the abyss. Lumps containing manganese, vital to the steel industry, and often containing nickel and cobalt also, cover some areas of the sea bottom. We knew of these nodules from photographs taken by Dr. Ewing and others, and recently the Navy brought up the first ton. Men in submarines equipped with mechanical arms and claws can scratch into the sea floor itself.

As submarines and torpedoes operate deeper and deeper, the more we learn about the depths, the better we will be at undersea warfare. The nature of the bottom, the topography of undersea mountain ranges, currents that submarines can ride, all need to be studied for military uses. Eyewitnesses helped find the hull of the sunken U.S.S. *Thresher,* over a mile and a half down.

Off Florida, scuba (self-contained underwater breathing apparatus) divers have poked about in the sand and uncovered two great hauls of Spanish riches: pieces of eight, gold bars, silver, jewelry, porcelain. Altogether, the National Geographic Society's *School Bulletin* estimates, sinking ships have carried down with them one-fifth of all the gold and silver mankind ever has mined. Eyewitnesses can help salvage modern sunken vessels or their cargoes, which are far more valuable than those of older treasure ships. One outfit has recovered $7 million in bullion sunk during World War II off Australia.

There is adventure ahead in the depths of the sea, adventure beyond any dreamed up by Jules Verne in *Twenty Thousand Leagues Under the Sea.* Through the windows of a deep-diving submarine men soon may witness a titanic struggle between monsters 1,500 feet down in the ocean—a battle between the 60-foot-long sperm whale (Herman Melville's famous Moby Dick was an albino sperm) and the 10-armed giant squid, *Architeuthis,* whose longest tentacles may extend as much as 35 feet beyond a 20-foot body. The squid, say Lorus and Margery Milne, has a 14-inch eye. No man has ever seen such a fight. No live giant squid, in fact, has ever been taken. We know the battles occur because sperm whales have been caught with circular scars or wounds from the suckers on the squids' tentacles on their skin, and inside the whales' stomachs have been found pieces of squid tentacles up to 19 feet long. Eyewitnesses aboard such a submarine could encounter, 3,300 feet down on the continental slopes off Japan, the monstrous Japanese spider crab, a creature taken by commercial fishermen in the area. The crab often is 6 feet across. The American Museum of Natural History exhibits a specimen 10 feet across, and calls the crab "the largest living arthropod" (a joint-legged animal).

Eyewitnesses on the bottom of shallow seas can discover new oil and gas fields and sulfur deposits, invaluable substances in this age of petroleum and chemistry. They can for the first time survey visually routes for submarine cables. They could help find the way for, and help construct, that prospective new wonder of the world: the thirty-mile tunnel—or chunnel, as it is called—beneath the English Channel. They can help bring up from shallow seas many things the growing world population needs that are known to be there, such as phosphorite for fertilizer, iron, chromite, gold (off Alaska), titanium (off Florida and North Carolina), platinum (off the west coast of the United States), diamonds (off southwest Africa), and tin (off Malaysia).

"Who hath desired the Sea?" Rudyard Kipling asked. The answer today is the men moving into the depths, from the continental shelves out to the midocean abysses. They are beginning the biggest job of exploration that exists on our own planet, the earth. The ocean depths are measured in cubic units, like space—they are, in fact, called inner space. The sea, on the average, is 12,556 feet, or almost 2½ miles deep. Altogether, there are 331 million cubic miles of "salt water unbounded," as Kipling called it, to explore. This is 15 times the cubic measure of all the land above sea level. These cubic miles of salt water cover 70.8 percent, over seven-tenths, of the globe. This is a staggering amount of unexplored territory: The oceans cover an area twice that of Mars. The floor of the Pacific alone is vaster than the entire surface of the moon.

As Ronald I. Currie puts it in *Seas, Maps, and Men:* "Considering that the sea covers the greater part of the earth's surface, it would be difficult to overestimate its future use to man."

The First Submarine
to Dive Over a Mile

THE SMALL American submarine actually touched the bottom at 6,000 feet, over a mile beneath the surface. She had made by far the deepest submarine dive ever. She not only touched the Atlantic floor, her pilot parked her there. She was the U.S. Navy's *Alvin,* the world's first deep-diving submarine, and he was William O. Rainnie, Jr., of the Woods Hole Oceanographic Institution, the first submarine skipper to put his craft on the ground that far down.

At this deepest penetration of the sea by a submarine, Rainnie switched on his floodlights. With Copilot Marvin J. McCamis, also of Woods Hole, he peered out through portholes that let the men see ahead and below. Under the light, they saw a gray, rocky region such as had never been explored by man.

That was a dramatic moment in July 1965. It was the first actual observation of the deep bottom from a submarine. It was man's first look at things seen before only from a bathyscaphe or by an underwater camera or hauled up by a deep-water dredge or corer. It was one of the moments when man, having reached the depths, began firsthand the exploration of the bottom of the sea.

The *Alvin* and her crew, consisting of Rainnie and McCamis, returned to the surface without incident. Her dive was every bit as important in the ocean as a two-man Gemini flight is in space. As spaceships are man's new tools for exploring the universe, so *Alvin* is one of his magnificent new tools for exploring the sea around him. She showed for the first time that men could build submarines to take them into the depths of the ocean. But already she has company. A second U.S. deep-diving submarine, the *Aluminaut* (Chapter 8), in November 1965 dived down to 6,250 feet in the Atlantic.

Alvin's dive is a striking indication that the way is open to the depths of the sea. It was not easy for men to open the way to the depths. The effort, which began before World War II, had taken years of labor and many descents into the ocean by two Americans, William Beebe and Otis Barton. In a steel ball called a bathysphere, which they could not control and which swung like a pendulum at the end of a long line to the surface, Beebe and Barton climaxed their prewar efforts by descending a half-mile down. They were the undersea equivalents of John Glenn, who made America's first Mercury trip into space.

Alvin is a craft that, like a Mercury or Gemini spaceship, would have been impossible in any age earlier than this one. She is short and squat. Only 22 feet long, 8 feet in beam, she displaces 13 long tons. She carries a 1,200-pound payload. Into this small craft has gone our knowledge of the depths gained from bathyspheres and bathyscaphes (the only deep-diving devices before today's deep-diving submarines), knowledge gained from nuclear and diesel-and-electric submarines, knowledge developed in engineering, in marine architecture, in electronics, and in the U.S. space program. New strong materials went into *Alvin*. Her 7-foot-diameter inner pressure hull, which carries and protects her two-man crew, is of high-strength steel, 1.33 inches thick. It *has* to be tough. The pressure upon each square inch at a depth of 6,000 feet is 2,750 pounds. Like the bathysphere and like the pressure hull of a bathyscaphe, *Alvin*'s pressure hull is a sphere, the best shape to resist the pressure of the depths. The hull was built in two halves and welded at its equator by Hohn & Clay in Houston, Texas. *Alvin*'s outer hull is fiber glass. It does not keep out the water; the sea is allowed to wash through *Alvin* everywhere except inside the pressure hull.

Connections between the inside and outside of the pressure hull are electrical, with the wires passing through especially designed fittings. Should it ever be necessary, *Alvin*'s crew can disconnect the pressure hull from the outer hull and rise to the surface. In case of trouble in shallow water, the men can escape in scuba gear.

Alvin was sponsored by the Office of Naval Research. The Navy's Bureau of Ships helped prepare performance specifications. The Applied Sciences Division of Litton Industries (formerly the Electronics Division of General Mills, Inc.) designed and built her. She is operated for the Navy by the Woods Hole Oceanographic Institution and is named for Allyn Vine, a Woods Hole scientist and a strong proponent of manned underwater vehicles. Rear Admiral J. K. Leydon, Chief of Naval Research, calls *Alvin* an "exciting new tool for conducting research in the ocean."

Her performance is what makes *Alvin* an "exciting new tool." Bathyscaphes have dived far deeper; one reached a depth of over six miles in 1960. But fundamentally bathyscaphes are elevators to lower men down and haul them up. They cannot move about the bottom to any extent. *Alvin* can. Electric motors encased in oil drive her at 1½ to 3½ knots and let her cover a range of 15 miles before she comes up. And that may be 24 hours after she submerges. Bathyscaphes, furthermore, are no more controlled by the men in them than were our earliest manned Mercury spaceships. *Alvin,* like any other submarine, is controlled by her pilots. She climbs, dives, turns, hovers, sails ahead or astern—all upon order from the pilot or copilot.

Alvin's large main propeller at her stern is turned from side to side to steer her just as you can steer a small boat by turning an outboard motor. A complete 360-degree turn can be made in less than *Alvin*'s length in about 45 seconds. Two small propellers, one on each side just to the rear of the 5-foot-high conning tower can thrust *Alvin* up or down or help push her ahead or astern. She can go astern about as fast as she can travel forward. All three propellers are controlled by an airplane-type control stick inside the pressure hull.

The heaviest metal, mercury, which is also the only liquid metal under normal temperatures, is used as trimming material on *Alvin.* Pumps move the mercury to a bow tank and thus point her nose down so she will descend, or move the mercury to a stern tank and so put her stern down to help her climb. Buoyancy is added by pumping oil from aluminum spheres (tanks) into collapsible rubber bags located in the seawater flowing through *Alvin* inside her fiber-glass outer hull. Oil is lighter in weight than water, and so these bags constitute a sort of underwater balloon. "As oil is pumped from the spheres into the rubber bags," explained Robert W. Morse, Assistant Secretary of the Navy for Research and Development, "the buoyancy is increased because the amount of seawater displaced by the vehicle is increased while the weight of the vehicle remains the same."

Dr. Earl E. Hays, head of the *Alvin* project, started to test the submarine in late 1964. At Woods Hole she began short, shallow dives, in water no deeper than 80 feet. In the spring of 1965 *Alvin* was transported to Port Canaveral, Florida, where more shallow dives were performed. Then she was moved to the Bahamas. Here, among other dives, she made one of 7,500 feet. There were no men inside, nor was *Alvin* independent of her mother barge on the surface, during this one; she was lowered by a rope.

Her mother barge is a catamaran—a barge with two hulls. The barge lifts *Alvin* out of the sea and transports her into position for a dive. The barge, in turn, is towed by a tug.

On July 20, 1965, the tug, barge, and *Alvin* had arrived in position for her dive to the bottom of the sea. She was off Andros Island in the Bahamas, 120 miles southeast of Miami.

The barge launched *Alvin* into the sea at 10:37. At 10:54 Rainnie and McCamis began their dive. Down *Alvin* went into the Tongue of the Ocean, a great canyon in the Western Bahamas, a dead-end canyon a mile deep. The Tongue of the Ocean is hemmed in on three sides by shoals, shallow water, and islands, is therefore unusually quiet, and will be used by the Navy for testing weapons and sound equipment.

Every 1,000 feet Rainnie stopped to be sure all systems were functioning normally. Thus taking his time, he was 2 hours 43 minutes bringing *Alvin* to the sea floor—he made a much slower dive than will be normal.

At 1:37 *Alvin* was on the bottom of the Tongue of the Ocean, 6,000 feet down.

At this deepest penetration of the sea by a man-carrying submarine, Rainnie turned on the outside lights. At a visibility of 30 to 40 feet, McCamis and he saw rock outcroppings.

In possessing portholes to look through, *Alvin* is unlike most subs, which have no windows. Skippers of most submarines have to use their periscopes and floodlights or television to behold the sea around them. *Alvin* has TV, too; she can also feel around with echo sounding and with sonar, like other submarines. Her sonar is two-way: It tells her how far above the floor she is, and how far beneath the surface of the sea. She has a mechanical arm which can be dropped off as a crab can shed a claw if it gets tangled in something.

Rainnie and McCamis checked out everything. Rainnie contacted the surface barge by sonar telephone. "Everything works beautifully," he said. *"Alvin* has exceeded all expectations."

After 27 minutes on the bottom the men rose to the surface. There they met a rough sea, due to a thunderstorm and 25-knot winds. *Alvin* was successfully picked up by her barge.

Rainnie and McCamis were safe. The trip that had opened up a new era for all mankind, as men for the first time in control of their own deep-diving submarine penetrated to the deep Atlantic floor, was officially described as "uneventful."

Alvin is the first submarine designed and built to go far down in the abyss. At 6,080.2 feet, or one nautical mile, the maximum depth *Alvin* is designed for, she enters a cold—around 40 degrees

Fahrenheit—inky black—except for the flashing lights of sea creatures—world, where the waters are sometimes motionless, sometimes move. In 1957 off Charleston, South Carolina, in the northward-flowing Gulf Stream, an American-British oceanographic expedition dropped Swallow depth floats set to float to a depth of around 6,500 feet. The floats traveled south. The surprising discovery that resulted was that beneath the Gulf Stream there is a current flowing in the opposite direction—southward—at speeds ranging from 2 to 8 miles a day. The submarine *Aluminaut* later confirmed, during deep-dive tests, the existence of this current.

At 6,000 feet down, *Alvin* reaches the home of some of the most amazing animals on the globe. She will have gone deeper than most whales are known to dive (whales have been found entangled in cables over 3,000 feet deep); far below the levels where surface or near-surface creatures like sharks, dolphins, turtles, game fish, and most familiar fish live out their lives. One animal that you find on the beach you can also come upon 6,000 feet down: the starfish. In the deep sea, however, there are many starfishes not seen on the shoreline. There are big ones, up to 32 inches across, and there are ones that have developed the skill of moving across the sea floor by running at up to 100 feet an hour on the tips of their arms instead of moving by dragging themselves along.

Codfish, deep-sea soles, flounders, saberfish, and turbot are on *Alvin*'s way down, at 1,000 to 4,000 feet. There are squid at *Alvin*'s 6,000-foot depth that are translucent like jellyfish, soft like jellyfish, and that possess weak muscles. One has a left eye much bigger than its right. There is an octopus, the only blind octopus men have found, so fragile and gelatinous, according to C. P. Idyll of the University of Miami's Institute of Marine Science, in *Abyss,* that you could mistake it for a jellyfish.

The 6,000-foot level is the home of many of the angler fish, the "fish that fish." They lure their prey, since they possess fishing lines and lures as part of their equipment. The angler, usually alone, floats almost motionless, perhaps fluttering or twitching the bait at the end of its line. Once a copepod or fish gets close, the angler gulps it down. The angler's stomach can expand to hold a fish as big as or bigger than itself. The swallowing champion of all time probably was the angler *Melanocetus johnsoni,* caught by the *Dana* expedition of 1920–22, which had swallowed a lantern fish, *Lampanyctus crocodylus,* twice as long as itself.

There are brotulids, fishes with big heads and long pointed tails, from a few inches to three feet long, in *Alvin*'s operating zone. A brotulid has a lateral-line system (a row of sense organs along its sides) so sensitive that it can detect currents produced by nearby creatures as they swim or feed, or even breathe. There are rattails at 6,000-foot depths. These, like the brotulids, are fish with big heads and long (rat) tails. There are deep-sea eels, with the long snake shape of the common eel. There are spiny eels, not really eels at all, but long thin fishes. They have been caught at depths of 6,500 feet and more, and probably eat what they can find in the mud of the bottom: hydroids, starfish, sponges, small squids. In the deep sea, not in the shallow water, are the biggest of all sea urchins, crabs, and isopods. Isopods on land include the quarter-inch pill bug and the European wood louse. Six thousand feet down they grow to 6 or 8 inches in diameter. Also in deep waters are the biggest sea spiders, ostracods, swimming pteropods (midwater snails), and tailed tunicates.

The middle depths of the ocean, where the *Alvin* travels, are believed by scientists to be the best-lighted of the dark depths. The animals of this region seem themselves to possess more light organs that make brighter light than the animals either above or below them in the sea. Light from the angler fishes attracts prey to their lines and lures. Some anglers can actually flash in separate colors, red, white, and blue. Deep-water squid, some of which glow themselves, and deep-water shrimp squirt luminous clouds into the water. In the case of both, the clouds may be smoke screens to enable the squid or shrimp to escape. One squid flashes blue and yellow lights. Another has lights at the very end of its tentacles.

William Beebe made a study of the fish around Bermuda, in depths of 1,000 to 1,300 feet and more, through which *Alvin* will pass. During the 1930's he studied 115,747 individual fish—still the most intensive survey of deep-sea fish made anywhere—and found that 66 percent of them had luminous organs.

The sparkling depths will be explored for the United States not only by men aboard *Alvin,* but also by scientists in other deep-diving submarines.

J. Louis Reynolds' *Aluminaut* can dive 15,000 feet, or almost three miles.

Deepstar 4000, built in France by Jacques-Yves Cousteau and the Westinghouse Corporation, has reached the United States. She has the capacity to dive 4,000 feet and has done so.

At the Naval Ordnance Test Station (NOTS), China Lake, California, the U.S. Navy, under Captain J. I. Hardy, has finished the *Moray,* one of the United States' latest deep-diving submersibles. She is a two-man vehicle, 33 feet long and 64 inches in diameter. She looks like a giant torpedo. Successfully tested with men aboard at Wilson Cove, San Clemente Island, she is planned to operate at 15 knots at depths up to 6,000 feet. Her two men sit inside a pressure-resistant aluminum sphere or cockpit which is surrounded by a streamlined outer hull of fiber-glass laminate. She will be used to study deep-ocean systems, and Navy scientists and engineers hope she will help improve sonar and underwater radio and television. Donald K. Moore, head of NOTS's Astrometrics Division, is responsible for *Moray* today.

The 2,000-foot-deep-capacity two-man *Deep Jeep* was also completed at China Lake. The Southwest Research Institute, San Antonio, Texas, and General Motors' research vessel *Swan* helped test *Deep Jeep;* Willis R. Forman is project manager. Navy scientists plan to investigate, aboard *Deep Jeep,* the ocean's biological layer below 1,000 feet—that is, below the deepest point reached by the diving saucer (Chapter 5). More deep-diving submarines are under construction or are being planned.

Russia has one or at most two deep-diving submarines. She also has a remodeled World War II submarine that is used as a research vessel, the *Severyanka*. She is equipped with portholes for viewing and photographing sea life, and has been out seeking herring for Russian fishing ships. She is believed to descend no deeper than 600 feet.

What men aboard the *Severyanka* have learned is enough to make fishery biologists hunger for more observations from submarines. Equipped with eight incandescent floodlights, she has come upon shoals of thousands of herrings, floating deeply in all kinds of positions including upside down (belly up). At about 7 A.M. the herring come to life, move down, and eventually disappear—not only beyond *Severyanka*'s range, but too deep to yield an echo on the echo sounder. The herring were apparently asleep, or lying doggo after eating, possibly because if they hang motionless they do not set up movements in the water that would lead predators to them. There was another surprise: Hydrophones showed that even when the herrings were inert they were chattering like starlings. They make noises like a man whistling or a rat squeaking. The *Severyanka* found young herrings in oval-shaped shoals measuring 100 by 164 feet. The shoals were between 131 and 164 feet apart and from 260 to 360 feet down. Older fishes in larger shoals were farther down. Diving into what her echo sounder indicated was a shoal of herrings, the *Severyanka*'s men saw nothing; when she went deeper, they saw only an occasional fish. It seemed that perhaps the herrings had lookouts that warned them, and that the shoal moved away without hesitation upon receiving a warning.

The Russians are reported to have built a five-man, 1,000-foot-depth submarine, and a smaller model that will permit men to crawl out when the ship is submerged. *Sea Secrets* has reported they are lowering men and women 1,500 feet in a diving bell, or hydrostat, where they hang suspended to observe migrating fish.

But the United States is ahead in submarines that reach the

depths of the sea. *Alvin* herself will be kept busy with engineering and scientific experiments and a number of deep dives. Specifically, she will—of all things—explore the depths for traces of ancient man. Fossilized teeth of the great hairy mammoth and the mastodon—both prehistoric, elephantlike monsters—have been hauled up by fishermen off New York, in Chesapeake Bay, and on Georges Bank. Now *Alvin* is to seek signs of early men who presumably hunted the beasts—spear points, human bones, and piles of oyster shells. Says Dr. Kenneth O. Emery of Woods Hole about *Alvin*'s forthcoming scientific program: "It will make oceanography as exciting as exploring the moon."

What happens when an impenetrable part of the earth is rendered accessible by new transportation? William Beebe, who first used the bathysphere to reach a half mile beneath the sea, had an answer: "Every corner of man's mind susceptible to enthusiasm or accumulated curiosity is aroused to highest pitch."

PART II

Man Prowls the Continental Shelf

The First Men Roam
the Bottom of the Sea

TO DIVE DEEPER than a man has ever dived, to stay longer than he has ever stayed on the bottom of the sea: these are the goals of Jon Lindbergh, son of the aviator Charles A. Lindbergh, and a handful of American and European divers. New methods and equipment permit Lindbergh and the others to roam the ocean floor at far greater depths than any men before them.

Off the Pacific coast Lindbergh and his associates, in teams of two men each, have made many descents to the sea bottom of over 240 feet. Each time they have spent more than 40 minutes there. In the Atlantic, Lindbergh and Robert Stenuit descended to 432 feet and stayed down two days. Their future plans include dives of 632 feet, 800 feet, 1,000 feet, and even deeper.

Other men, inside bathyspheres or bathyscaphes or deep-diving submarines, have descended far deeper, but they could not leave their protecting shells. Lindbergh and his companions ride down to the bottom inside diving bells—thick steel spheres or cylinders— and then step out and walk around.

Then they remain on the sea floor for a long time, up to a matter of hours. An eight-hour workday on the bottom is one of their objectives.

"Men are going to have to live and work on the bottom of the sea," Captain Ray M. Pitts, U.S. Navy (Retired), and one of Lindbergh's bosses, said. "Men are going to have to stay there for long periods. We are demonstrating that we can."

"We don't know," Lindbergh told me, "how deep we can dive. Two thousand feet is looked at by some men as a possible likely limit. But this is arbitrary.

"With a good gas mixture, and with a knowledge of decompression—we're still refining that—it may be possible to dive 3,000 feet. As we try to go deeper, the big problem will be decompression— we'll have to know how long to stay in the decompression chamber before we leave it.

"I have been diving since I started in the Navy 10 or 11 years ago. I've done a lot of work on drilling and completing oil wells. I once helped salvage a kelp barge off California. Recently, I've been putting in an 8-foot-diameter sewer line off Seattle." Seawater, one of the most effective germ killers known, destroys 80 percent of the nonmarine bacteria in sewage in the first half hour. That's the reason why sewage is piped or hauled aboard garbage scows out to sea.

"What does a diver see as he works on the sea floor?" Jon Lindbergh repeated my question. "You often see long chains of small animals strung together, ribbonlike, sea-serpent-like things—you see hundreds of them in a day. You see ocean sunfish occasionally, the big, round, 8-foot-diameter *Mola molas*—there are a lot of these off California. You see occasional sharks. You see octopuses if you look for them in the rocks. Last week I saw a 19-footer on the sewer line!

"We don't have many close calls on the bottom. We stay away from incidents."

Captain Pitts and Lindbergh work for a new company, Ocean Systems, Inc., a private firm organized to do work of all kinds on the ocean bottom.

Captain Pitts says their divers can reach the seabed anywhere on the almost unexplored continental shelves. These shelves run from the water's edge out to the continental slopes, where the bottom drops off into the deep sea.

To pioneer is a habit in the Lindbergh family. In May 1927, when Jon's father, Charles A. Lindbergh, became the first flyer to pilot a plane nonstop from New York to Paris, he prepared the way for all of today's long-distance aviation.

Jon Lindbergh, too, has a "first" to his credit. He and Robert Stenuit in 1964 became the first men to spend 49 hours in one stretch at a depth of 432 feet near Nassau, in the Atlantic. That was the longest deep dive ever made.

On their Nassau dive Lindbergh and Stenuit descended in a metal diving chamber to the sea floor. Once on the bottom, they lived in an inflatable, floorless, 6-by-9-foot rubber tent, or house. The breathing gas in this underwater home was kept under a pressure equal to that of the surrounding water; therefore, no water could enter. Ed Link, inventor of aviation's Link trainer and now an ocean explorer himself, designed the house and named it SPID (Submersible Portable Inflatable Dwelling).

Lindbergh and Stenuit left and entered the SPID whenever they chose. Their cans of food were squashed by the pressure, but the food inside was edible. They returned to the surface, spent four days in a decompression chamber, and were in no way harmed by their long dive.

One reason they, unlike the tin cans, came through unscathed was that the great pressure of the depths is turning out not to be the menace to men it was once feared. The human body, unlike tin cans, is now believed to be no more compressible than the body of a fish. This is because the body is largely made up of almost incompressible liquids. Mammals, including humans, are expected not only to be able to survive at great depths, but to experience no great difficulty in working in them. Ocean Systems makes experiments on dry land, in Tonawanda, New York, in a pressure chamber—a big tank in which men and animals undergo the equivalent of the pressures of great depths. But the men and animals stay dry because the tank is filled with compressed air or gas mixtures instead of water. Mice tested by Ed Link in the dry-land tank have shown that mammals can survive a pressure equivalent to 5,000 feet (almost a mile) deep.

Late in 1965 Arthur D. Noble and Robert W. Christensen lived inside the dry-land tank at a pressure of 304.2 pounds per square inch, which corresponds to that found at 650 feet beneath the sea, for 48 hours and 2 minutes—a record length of time for men in a simulated (i.e. dry-land) dive at a pressure equal to what they would experience 650 feet down.

What to breathe is a problem for divers. Below 300 feet breathing a regular mixture of air gives men what is called nitrogen narcosis; their minds get fuzzy, and they quickly become unreliable. So Lindbergh and the other Ocean Systems' divers inhale a mixture of oxygen, helium, and a small percentage of nitrogen. Breathing this mixture makes men more efficient in deep water, but their voices sound high-pitched and garbled like Donald Duck. A device called a helium speech converter makes their voices understandable. For 30 minutes during their two-day stay inside Ocean Systems' dry-land tank at a simulated 650-foot pressure, Noble and Christensen breathed a neon-oxygen mixture. With it their voices were clear. Each man in turn recited Lincoln's Gettysburg Address, and each could be easily understood.

Ocean Systems and other organizations engaged in diving activities are pursuing research on what the pressure of the depths will do to men. In the September-October 1965 issue of *Sea Frontiers* F. G. Walton Smith, president of the International Oceanographic Foundation, points out that we don't know the basic physiology and biochemistry of tissues and cell membranes and metabolic processes under high pressure. "It is already known," he says, "that certain enzyme systems may be suppressed or slowed down considerably by the effect of pressure. [An enzyme is a complex body chemical.] To what extent does protoplasm itself change and, for instance, become more viscous under pressure? It is very probable that some entirely new and unsuspected biological limitation to man's deep diving may be discovered that has nothing to do with gas mixtures, narcosis, and the bends."

The divers working with Lindbergh include, in addition to Stenuit, Whitey Stefens, Bill Gianotti, Jack Strickland, Ken Lingyel, Bill Bossert, and Gene Handelman. All belong to a division of Ocean Systems known as Offshore Divers. Lindbergh is manager of the Seattle, Washington, branch; there are other branches at Santa Barbara, California, and at Morgan City, Louisiana. Ocean Systems, Inc., is owned by Union Carbide Corporation and General Precision Equipment Corporation. The Ocean Systems executives include Ed Link; Rear Admiral Edward C. Stephan, U.S. Navy (Retired), the first man ever appointed oceanographer of the Navy; Captain Ray Pitts, and Dan Wilson, the head of Offshore Divers.

Perhaps as much as any other man, Dan Wilson has made the longest, deepest dives in the world possible. In effect he opened up the whole deep-diving business. He pioneered, for example, in developing the Navy-invented helium-oxygen-nitrogen breathing techniques. Wilson and Link also designed the diving bells, or elevators, the men use. Captain Pitts described one of them to me.

"We use a diving bell, the *Purisima*," Captain Pitts said, "named for a point on the California shore, Purisima Point. The *Purisima,* which consists of two ball-shaped chambers, each 6 feet 6 inches in diameter, is really an elevator. It carries the divers, one or two in each chamber, up and down. It has no propeller, and no means of propelling itself.

"As the *Purisima* descends—it can sink 600 feet in 10 minutes—the lower chamber is pressurized up to the point where its pressure matches that of the depth to which it is going. Then, at a depth of 600 feet, for example, the men inside are already under the same pressure they will meet in the surrounding water.

"When the *Purisima* comes back to the surface—it can rise 600 feet in 5 minutes, or at a speed twice that at which it went down; it has been given a rapid ascending speed in case of emergency— it may be hauled out of the water and placed in a small space on the deck of the barge. The divers remain inside as long as necessary while decompression goes on. The *Purisima* is its own decompression chamber."

The spheres are heated and have water, food, lights, and toilets. They have, independent of connections to the surface, oxygen supplies and battery power and a system to remove carbon dioxide exhaled by the men.

The *Purisima* is hauled down to the bottom by a weighted basket. The weighted basket can be dropped from within *Purisima,* which then will rise to the surface. If the main cable to the surface is lost, it can climb entirely on its own. Every possible thing has been done to make the *Purisima* system, or Advanced Diving System, as it is called, foolproof and accident-proof. It will fail safe, if it fails at all.

A single, main cable connects *Purisima* to a barge on the surface. The cable carries electricity and compressed gas. It also carries telephone wires and TV sound and pictures. There is a TV camera in the ceiling of each sphere focused on the men inside, so that men on the barge can watch them. Once outside on the bottom, the divers carry TV cameras connected by cable to the cable in the *Purisima,* and thus send video images to the surface.

The divers have another new tool: a hand-held, transistorized, underwater sonar that can lead a diver to an object as small as a five-gallon paint can 30 feet away.

Out on the ocean bed the divers receive the gas they breathe from a short hose coming from the *Purisima*—no long, bulky, cumbersome, and entangling hose to the surface.

To light up the depths for his divers, Captain Pitts provides them with what he terms the most efficient underwater light yet. It spreads a blue-green glow that illuminates the depths. Men can see very well with it. But the divers hate it; the color seems too eerie to them. So lights of other colors are being tried.

In another diving system used by Ocean Systems the diving elevator consists not of two spheres but of a sphere on top and a cylinder on the bottom. For some dives a single sphere is used by itself.

Tests with the *Purisima* have shown how anyone—anyone at all —may go down into the sea for a look around through its round windows, or portholes. Recently men in their shirt sleeves without any diving gear whatever were lowered in the top sphere to a depth of 240 feet, while being kept under normal atmospheric pressure. They were petroleum engineers inspecting an offshore well. This was the first time such men have ever been able to see an offshore well that they had to repair, and guide and supervise divers at work. In the future it may become routine for anyone to be lowered in a diving bell for a peep at the sea floor.

The depth of 240 feet reached by the shirt-sleeved engineers, who remained inside the *Purisima,* is about as deep as any divers breathing air have been able to work efficiently up until now, before the new gas mixtures, before the design of the *Purisima* itself, and before the pioneering efforts of Lindbergh and others to go far deeper.

Before 1964 there had been only a few occasions when divers reached depths outside of their diving chambers comparable to those at which Lindbergh and his teammates work. That will give you an idea of how revolutionary the performances planned by Ocean Systems are. In 1945, Arne Zetterström of England reached 533 feet. In 1948, William Bollard of the Royal Navy got to 547 feet. In 1949, eleven U.S. Navy divers stayed at 560 feet for a few minutes. In 1956 George Wookey of a British diving team reached a depth of 600 feet off Norway. He used an advanced form of standard diving gear (a normal diving-suit with heavy helmet) and breathed oxygen-helium. He stayed down only a few minutes, and did little useful work. In 1961, a Swiss diver, Hannes Keller, who had developed his own mixture of gases to breathe, and a journalist, Kenneth MacLeish of *Life,* descended 728 feet. In 1962, Keller and a British writer named Peter Small, in a boiler-shaped chamber, reached 1,000 feet near Santa Catalina Island, off California. Then, said Keller, he opened the chamber, swam out, and planted United States and Swiss flags on the bottom. He was outside the chamber no longer than from 30 seconds to 2 minutes. As soon as he returned to the chamber the men started back up. Something went wrong; the chamber lost pressure; the men had to switch from breathing a special mixture of gases to breathing air. Small was dead when they took him out of the chamber. In 1963, both Royal Navy and U.S. Navy divers again cracked 500 feet.

The pace of diving was stepped up in 1964 and 1965. In 1964, Divcon Associates made a 525-foot dive lasting 25 minutes to repair an oil-well head. During 1965 a team of eight British Royal Navy divers, working in the Mediterranean Sea off Toulon, France, successfully worked at 600 feet. They sawed metal, took movies, and made scientific observations. They went down in a diving bell that, like *Purisima,* was its own compression chamber, stepped out in frogmen's suits and breathing apparatus, and stayed out in the sea for an hour. They were under a pressure of 280 pounds per square inch, 17 times the atmospheric pressure on the ground. They were safe from being crushed because they breathed oxygen-helium at a pressure equal to that of the water around them. The British divers were preparing the way for exploration of the bottom of the North Sea in a search for oil and gas.

Now Lindbergh and other United States and European divers, using the *Purisima* or similar equipment, are out to make depths of 600 to 1,000 feet routine and to remain much longer walking and working on the sea floor at those depths and, as Lindbergh has pointed out, eventually at even greater depths. The *Purisima* has been tested without divers in it and has proved to be safe at as much as 1,800 feet down.

"We are showing," says Captain Pitts, "that the divers can stay at different levels for as long as we want them to.

"If man is to conquer his new frontier, the deep sea, man must live and work forever at these deep depths. Our goal is to show he can. We are," Captain Pitts concludes, "doing a type of job man has not done before."

You Can Explore

in a Midget Submarine

THE AVERAGE MAN and his family already can go to the bottom of the sea. They may make the voyage aboard a submarine. On Lake Geneva, Switzerland, Jacques Piccard has been piloting the *Auguste Piccard,* the first submarine to carry tourists. The *Auguste Piccard* holds as many as 40 passengers and has taken 25,000 people on 850 dives. The 93½-foot-long submarine has been reaching an average depth of 300 feet.

Still another way in which they may survey the shallow depths of the sea and the seabed itself is by means of a small one-, two-, or six-man submarine. The United States, for the first time, has a fleet of these tiny submersibles. At least four dozen have been built already, and more are under construction. Most of the little submarines are privately owned. They are being built by a number of companies in widely separated cities, and so this fleet of small submarines has grown without attracting much attention.

In fact, the day may soon come when you will own your own submarine. This sounds impossible to believe. But it is only since World War II that the United States has become a nation of motorboat owners. This is largely because of improved outboard motors, all very dependable, some of which you can even tote yourself.

In the future, in a nearer future than you might expect, submarines may become a common sight in the garages of American homes. How near at hand is the day when you will cruise the depths in your own family submarine may be indicated by some sales literature I have just received from the American Submarine Company of Lorain, Ohio.

This brochure itself is a first in oceanography: it attempts to sell a submarine directly to you and me—to the man in the street. Here is an American company peddling submarines to private citizens, not to the Navy, or the government, or scientific institutions.

"MAYBE," the pamphlet is headlined, "YOU NEED A SUBMARINE. THERE ARE," it says in big type, "RICH REWARDS UNDER THE SEA!"

The pamphlet describes two submarines the company makes. The Amersub 300 it calls "a practical two-man dry submarine at moderate cost! The world's first low-cost, truly practical underwater craft! The Amersub 300 is perfect for the individual as well as the scientist or industrial user. It is fully equipped . . . and is capable of depths to 300 feet. Versatile and compact, it can be towed to the launch site as easily as an outboard."

The brochure gives specifications of the Amersub 300: Pressure hull: Of high-strength welded steel. Length: 13 feet. Width: 4 feet 2 inches. Height: 4 feet 9 inches. Speed: 1 to 6 knots. Range: 12 to 16 miles. Weight: 2,200 pounds. Operational mode: Neutrally buoyant. Power source: Four 6-volt, heavy duty, rechargeable lead acid batteries connected for series or parallel operation. Motor: A three-horsepower electric propulsion motor drives a conventional propeller shaft. Operational controls: Aircraft-type stick for operating diving planes and surfacing; another stick for rudder control. There is an eight-hour fresh air supply. You can surface either by driving the Amersub up with its propeller, by blowing ballast or trim tanks, or by releasing the lead keel. The Amersub 300 has two conning towers with one-inch-thick Plexiglas windows all the way around. Here sit the two men she carries, one in each conning tower.

The other submarine in the line, one with a 600-foot-depth capacity, is the Amersub 600. This one, it says right here in the advertising booklet, is "to take you where the action is." The 600 is labeled the "compact challenger of the continental shelf!"

"A whole new world is yours!" the manufacturer says. "With 600-feet depth capacity, a 16-hour fresh air supply for two people and a comprehensive selection of specialized optional equipment, the Amersub 600 is eminently suited to simple or complex under-sea missions. Controls and handling techniques are sufficiently sim-plified so that the operator need not be an 'old salt.' Yet the 600 gets you where you want to be in complete safety."

The 600 has only one conning tower. One man, the pilot, sits here. The other man, a passenger, lies prone and looks out through an 8-inch Plexiglas port in the bottom forward.

The continental shelf, for which the 600 is designed, is the sea-bed beneath the shallow depths that surround the continents. The water over the continental shelf averages something over 600 feet deep. Besides being the sea floor that the average man is most likely to reach, it is the sea floor that will be most extensively explored first as man enters the sea. Jon Lindbergh and other divers are opening it up. Practically all midget submarines are designed to operate over the shelf.

There is good reason. The continental shelves of the world total 10 percent of the globe's area. They are an almost unknown region as large as Africa.

Under an international agreement signed in 1964, the U.S. con-tinental shelves have been acquired by the United States for eco-nomic development. This is, says the Coast and Geodetic Survey of the Department of Commerce, "the most extensive territory to be added to the country since the Louisiana Purchase in 1803."

The shelf totals about 850,000 square miles—about one-fourth of the total U.S. land area. It extends from 10 to 300 miles off the U.S. coast; the narrow 10-mile shelf is off Hawaii and also off the Pacific coast, where the shelf stretches only 10 to 50 miles offshore. Off Alaska it extends 300 miles; off the Gulf of Mexico, 50 to

150 miles; off Cape Cod, 175 miles; off the South Atlantic States, 50 to 150 miles.

The agreement provides that the United States has sovereignty out to a depth of 200 meters, or 656 feet, and also has sovereignty beyond that depth wherever the natural resources of the shelves can be exploited by the United States.

"We should have a Lewis and Clark Expedition to the continental shelf," says Dr. Edward B. Shykind, associate staff director of the Federal Government's Interagency Committee on Oceanography.

Hundreds, even thousands, in the next few years will explore the continental shelf in scuba outfits, diving bells, or from the new fleet of midget submarines.

Another company is ready to provide you with your choice of a full line of individual submarines—an indication of how far the United States is along the road of providing an undersea craft for every garage. This is the Perry Submarine Builders, Inc., John H. Perry, Jr., president, of West Palm Beach, Florida.

A two-man Perry Cubmarine costs $29,000 (low enough for many yacht clubs or organizations to afford it) and can operate 150 feet down. Other Perry Cubmarines can submerge up to 600 feet, and one of them worked at that depth recently in the Tongue of the Ocean, the canyon in the Bahamas where the *Alvin,* the Navy's deep-diving submarine, made her record over-a-mile-deep trip.

One Perry Cubmarine has 18 portholes (no less) for looking around at the depths in any direction. The Cubmarine can tow a diver. It can easily be lifted out of the water. Fish and other reef dwellers, the Perry company says, are not disturbed by the submarine's presence. This would be contrary to the experience of Jacques-Yves Cousteau and Harold Edgerton, who, lowering their cameras into the Mediterranean and Indian Oceans, found that fish and other sea creatures fled from such strange objects. But the Perry Cubmarine people offer proof: They show a photograph of a barracuda apparently resting calmly beside one of their Cub-marines.

Now Perry is building a 1,500-foot-deep craft. The company is also studying how to take divers to the bottom in one of its sub-marines, let them step out onto the sea floor and work, then clamber back aboard and be transported back to the surface. A five-man Cubmarine with an underwater entrance and exit hatch for skin divers and an operating depth of 250 feet is available. It can cruise 500 miles.

The Perry organization is the United States agent for four small submarines made in West Germany. The 10-foot, 1,400-pound, one-man *Porpoise,* built by Graf Hagenburg, costs $3,995. It dives to 150 feet and was shown at the New York Motor Boat Show in 1965. The man in it sits in a Plexiglas dome with visibility all around him. The *Tigershark,* manufactured by Silverstar-Vertriebs-GMBH, carries two men to 115 feet down, is 17 feet 6 inches long, and costs $10,800. The *Bahamian* by Silverstar carries a pilot and five passengers, "for sightseeing," the advertising matter says. The *Florida* by Hagenburg carries a pilot and two passengers.

You can rent the *Porpoise* for around $100 a day, or about what a de luxe outing on a deep-sea fishing boat costs.

At Groton, Connecticut, the Electric Boat Division of General Dynamics, the builders of twenty-one nuclear submarines, have com-pleted their first two small submarines. The first, *Star I,* has a trans-parent dome and two lower 7-inch viewports of 1½-inch-thick Plexiglas. *Star I* can maintain its one-man crew for 18 hours. It dives 200 feet, travels at one knot, all out, and is battery-driven by two ¼-horsepower electric motors.

The second, the *Asherah,* was built for the University of Penn-sylvania. It was used, in cooperation with the National Geographic Society, for probing the ocean floor off the coast of Turkey during an archaeological expedition. *Asherah* can maintain a two-man crew for twenty-four hours, usually dives for ten. The submarine can dive to 600 feet, travels at 4 knots, and has moved on to the

Bureau of Commercial Fisheries in Hawaii, where it is being used to provide eyewitnesses the opportunity to observe the reactions of fish to different kinds of bait and tackle. Some of the Bureau's scientists, 500 feet down in *Asherah* off Oahu, recently found there the precious red coral used for jewelry—the rarer shades of this coral fetch up to $7,000 an ounce. At 600 feet down, she found commercially valuable skipjack tuna, not previously known to dive so deep. In some areas she found plankton 50 to 100 times as plentiful as formerly believed. She found numbers of large lobsters dwelling in crevices.

Electric Boat is now building *Star II,* a research submarine to dive to 1,200 feet, and *Star III,* which will dive to 2,000 feet.

Other small submarines in use today include the *Sportsman,* with a 300-foot-depth capacity, operated by the U.S. Bureau of Sport Fisheries and Wildlife, and the *Submaray,* made by the Hydrotech Company, Long Beach, California, which also can dive 300 feet.

Japan has come up with the *Aquamarine,* for two men in the crew and two scientists, to help grow marine plants and fish in farms on the continental shelf. You can even build your own two-man submarine: Jim Helle of Scripps has just done so. It took 16 months. What he has is a 9-foot-long by 4-foot-wide *Submanuat.* Made of marine plywood and fiber glass, *Submanaut* is driven by a 1½-horsepower battery-powered electric motor at 3 knots. In her bow there is a two-foot viewing port. *Submanaut* is designed to operate at 1,000 feet and has been pressure tested to 350 feet.

Many have had their first look at a small submarine at Chicago's Museum of Science and Industry. In its yard there has been displayed one of the small Japanese submarines of the type used in the attack on Pearl Harbor. The British Royal Navy in World War II also used 2- to 5-man submarines. They were called X-craft. Six of them crept into Alten Fjord, Norway, and from 200 yards away torpedoed and put out of action the German 35,000-ton *Tirpitz,* one of the hugest battleships that took part in World War II, and for a long time a menace to Allied convoys to Russia.

Today's small submarines are as vastly improved over the World War II X-craft as our nuclear submarines of today are over our World War II types.

Though one-family submarines may never be as common as automobiles, they may one day be as popular as motorboats. That day will be sped along by the actions of people like Marty Rubin, an insurance man from Livingston, New Jersey, who already owns a 16-foot cruiser runabout. Mr. Rubin took a look at the one-man German submarine at a New York boat show, and said, "What does it mean to me? It means I've got to start saving my money."

A Regular Ferry
Runs to the Sea Floor

THE TWO MEN—Larry Somers and André Laban—were stretched out on their stomachs on foam-rubber mattresses inside a two-man submarine. Just in front of the nose of each man was a small Plexiglas porthole through which he peered into the sea. What the men saw as they sailed over a submarine canyon off California surprised them: Vegetation grew straight out of the steep canyon walls. "Approaching the nearly vertical walls," their report said, "was like looking at the tops of trees in a forest from the air."

They were in the diving saucer sponsored by Westinghouse and designed by Captain Jacques-Yves Cousteau. The log said later: "They did not see what they expected to see. But then, that's why they were diving."

Off California and Lower California (Mexico) the diving saucer made the first continuous, long (six-month) probing of the continental shelf by a small submersible. Between November 1964 and April 1965, it made 125 dives in all. In it were the first American scientists to explore the offshore depths down to 1,000 feet on a regular schedule. What those eyewitnesses saw is an indication of what others will see as men and small submarines prowl offshore waters.

The diving saucer, named *Denise* and also called the *soucoupe* (French for "saucer"), is 9½ feet in diameter, 5½ feet high, and weighs 3½ tons. It is battery-driven and can remain underwater for four hours. It can keep the men in it safe for 48 hours if necessary. It is propelled by two water jets mounted on its sides, and its submerged speed is one knot, slightly over one mile an hour. It has a mechanical arm for picking up samples and a bucket for holding them. *Denise* usually carries a pilot and a scientist.

On its Pacific coast series of 125 dives the *soucoupe* was used by scientists from the Scripps Institution of Oceanography, the U.S. Navy Electronics Laboratory, the Pacific Missile Range, the Naval Missile Center, the Naval Ordnance Test Station, Pasadena Annex, and the Westinghouse Corporation.

Captain Cousteau had used the *soucoupe* for many dives in the Mediterranean and elsewhere before it was flown to the west coast of the United States. Some of the dives were off San Clemente Island off the California shore—a spot that will be remembered by Navy, Marines, and Army men of the Pacific amphibious forces during World War II. At that time San Clemente was used for training maneuvers and target practice.

For the pioneer U.S. submarine explorers aboard the diving saucer the question was simply, "What's down there?"

Often operating at far greater depths than scuba divers have ever reached, they were the first men to observe with their own eyes what the continental shelf and the bottom of the Pacific near the west coast is like.

Pilot Raymond (Canoe) Kientzy and Dr. Francis Shepard, Scripps professor of submarine geology, had their visibility cut at a depth of 700 feet by a huge number of fish in the early stages of growth. "In fact," Dr. Shepard said, "it was one thing that made visibility poor—there were just clouds of small fish."

Edward Winterer, a marine geologist and associate professor at the Scripps Institution, noticed from the small submersible a slight, previously unknown current in the sea around him. It was about one-fourth of a knot.

Winterer watched the placing of a current meter on the bottom to measure the current on a continuing basis. Because he could look at the meter being lowered, he could make sure that it was not put behind a big rock or in some other location where it could not function properly. This was an example of the usefulness of the diving saucer and of eyewitnesses beneath the sea.

Dr. Robert Dill, a geologist of the U.S. Navy Electronics Laboratory, went down with Pilot Kientzy and found the shallow bottom covered with squid eggs. They saw the female squid laying them. Farther down, 300 to 370 feet, the men found the bottom sand so hard that the diving saucer could raise itself up on its mechanical arm without leaving a mark on the sand. Visibility ranged from 6 inches to 60 feet as the men peered from the diving saucer's windows. They found a current of around four-tenths of a knot.

Dr. E. W. Fager made the first dive at night. A flashing neon light had been mounted on the outside of the diving saucer to attract attention when the saucer returned to the surface. The little submersible had trouble coming up. It got tangled in an old manila line. Dr. Fager and Pilot Kientzy dropped a 400-pound emergency weight, part of their ballast, as prescribed for just such an emergency. Up they came. The flashing light soon brought a boat to their assistance.

Art Flechsig, also of Scripps, was in Scripps Canyon when animal life was spotted. "The corals, crinoids, and sponges were colored yellow, white, and pink. Amongst these were small crabs swimming," he reported. There were large numbers of flatfish, or sand dabs, and an occasional shrimp or squid.

Off San Clemente, Dr. E. L. Buffington of the Electronics Laboratory went down and confirmed what electronic soundings had told about the contours of the sea floor. He saw concentrations of small sea urchins about the size of a quarter in great clusters, and large numbers of squid swimming around. They did not try to get out of the way of the *soucoupe*. Many movies were made of them. Buffington noted a "minute lacy network of animal trails all over the silt."

Joe Thompson and Canoe Kientzy made another dive, off Mexico, and found a canyon with steep, in some places vertical, granite walls. Moving over the canyon, they estimated that at one place it was no more than 20 feet wide, and so did not descend into it. They encountered a number of large fish, some 5 or 6 feet long—grouper and amber jack, or bonito. At about 400 feet Thompson observed a purple nudibranch, deeper than he supposed any lived. The nudibranch is a shell-less mollusk with a body like that of a slug. The men also found tube worms—marine worms that live in tubes of their own making. They seem to have no close relatives in the animal kingdom. One species of green tube worms up to 8 inches long has been discovered off California in colonies almost an acre in extent. In a colony 4 inches square G. E. and Nettie MacGinitie counted 281 tube worms. Thompson and Kientzy found gorgonians, or sea fans—colonies of animals that look like living flowers. Their branches line up on a flat plane shaped like a fan. The men found a number of big-eyed zooplankton—animals three-sixteenths of an inch long. This is large for plankton, which are mostly microscopic.

Jim Meldenhauer went down to inspect a possible site for an underwater observatory, a living museum of the sea—a place where one day you will be able to walk out beneath the sea and see for yourself the depths of the continental shelf. To build such an undersea observation post is a plan of the Scripps Institution. Meldenhauer looked over a preliminary site on Farnsworth Bank, which rises up spectacularly off the shelf west of Santa Catalina Island. This bank, located where the sea is 250 feet deep, reaches up to about 50 feet below the surface. Meldenhauer found rich and beautifully colored plants and animals on the bank's steep sides. Big boulders tend to clump on the bank and form undersea rock gardens. Visibility there was 75 feet, and it provided a spectacular show—a good place for the observatory.

Then there was "the day the monsters met." This was when the diving saucer encountered, in shallow water off San Clemente Island, the CURV (Cable-Controlled Underwater Recovery Vehicle), an unmanned vehicle. Men who watched on TV the meeting of the two sea-exploring machines say it was a dramatic confrontation. The CURV has sonar that can home in on an object and steer the CURV to it. It can also be commanded by underwater telephone. The saucer reached out its mechanical arm and attempted to shake hands with the articulated claw of the CURV. It looked, someone said, like a picture out of Jules Verne.

Yet when the diving saucer tried to pick up a torpedo in its claw, the task proved difficult; the pilot needed three hands. The pilot, André Laban, recommended simpler controls. The saucer later recovered a number of torpedoes, each costing $75,000. Later, off San Clemente, the saucer closed its claw on an octopus, which simply slipped out and hid in nearby rocks.

Back on another dive, Dr. Winterer spied hermit crabs by the thousands moving along the bottom, each one carrying his snail shell with him.

Art Flechsig made a dive on Coronado Bank, at nearly the diving saucer's maximum depth of 1,000 feet. He found flatfish, some up to 7 feet long, rockfish, and a crab holding a piece of white sponge in each hind leg.

Dr. Joseph R. Curray, a research geologist, must have thought he was in another world—as indeed he was: "The bottom sediment was a shelly muddy sand and was literally covered with thousands of Galatea crabs. These crabs were in constant motion, digging, fighting, and working on the bottom, stirring it up."

Robert F. Dill dived off Cabo (Cape) San Lucas, Mexico. Dill saw on the sea floor "an excellent index fossil . . . a Mexicali beer can. This brand arrived in San Lucas last year. It was half covered —thus showing quite accurately the amount of sediment deposited in about one year."

Off Lower California divers came upon a narrow sand strip, occasionally washed over by storms, which is known as Dying Pelican Beach. They found the name justified. Some of the pelicans there had become blind, probably from plummeting into the water to grab fish, and thus were helpless. One pelican had ripped its pouch so that it could not keep fish in its mouth to swallow. Canoe Kientzy sewed up the ripped skin of the torn pouch, then the diving-saucer men filled the pouch with fish. The pelican waddled away contentedly.

Dr. Richard Rosenblatt of the Scripps Institution found the diving saucer almost as good as scuba diving for studying the fish: "The only thing I couldn't do was stick my head under the rocks."

F. G. Wood dived in the saucer to observe seals and sea lions. He saw none, but did see a good many other things: "A large number of sea pens, which seemed to form a forest one to two feet high along the bottom." Sea pens are colonial animals whose size is usually a foot or so. Said the diving saucer's log: "Part way down the slope, Woodie saw a different population of some sort of invertebrate that he couldn't identify. They were a flexible-looking yellowish-brown in color and from 2 to 4 inches long by ⅛ inches in diameter. As they came along, they would retract into the bottom. . . . Some octopuses sat out on the sand as we had seen on previous dives. These were reddish-brown in color and sometimes lay in small depressions. It puzzled Woodie still why these apparently defenseless creatures are out on the sand so far from any protection."

On another dive, octopuses were observed churning up the sediment so busily that it seemed to be one way, previously unsuspected, of moving sediment along the bottom. Wood also noticed "a snail without a shell, perhaps 8 inches in length with two large horns, like antennae, over the eyes."

The last United States dive of the saucer was in Long Beach, California, harbor. "We all thought," the saucer's log records, "that in the muddy looking harbor it would be black and mucky . . . but to our surprise, we could see several feet to maybe six feet at times and managed to observe quite a few animals living on and in the bottom. Life in the sea seems to be just about everywhere . . . even in dirty harbors."

Westinghouse compiled statistics on the 125 submersions the little submarine had made. It had taken 50 scientists down for almost 3½ hours each. The dives had been reliable and regular. On the average 17½ dives a month were made instead of the hoped-for 15. The saucer had shown it could maintain its depth within one or two feet for 15 minutes at a time, and that it could maneuver in narrow canyons and in other tight quarters.

Requests were quick to come in to use the diving saucer for future assignments. Some oceanographers wanted it to study submerged beach features off Florida; others, to serve as an acoustically quiet platform at sea; others wanted to work in it deep in the Gulf Stream; and still others, to use it to team up with other submersibles. These first regularly scheduled trips show that men can depend on it, and can explore the depths in submersibles on a regular basis.

CHAPTER
6

*Scuba Divers Find
Treasure Millions*

IN A New York City swimming pool not long ago I turned myself into a porpoise. What I did showed how anyone can become a scuba diver and gain the ability to stay down a long time without tiring.

In the shallow end of the pool I scrambled face downward onto a wooden framework that looked something like an airplane. Its wingspan was 40 inches. The wings stuck out on either side of my chest. I put my feet into a contraption looking something like the tail of the plane. Across the rear end of the contraption lay a flat board resembling a plane's elevator. When you bent your knees, the board went up and down like a porpoise's tail. With the device, called the Aqueon, that porpoise tail can scoot you through the water faster than an Olympic swimmer.

It took me a few minutes to get the hang of the Aqueon. In swimming I was used to kicking my legs instead of just bending my knees. I never approached an Olympic swimmer's speed that day.

"Women and girls," said Calvin Gongwer, the Aqueon's inventor, looking pointedly at me, "learn quicker than men do." Gongwer's 18-year-old daughter Jean is a skilled swimmer with an Aqueon.

You can easily cruise on the Aqueon at $2\frac{3}{10}$ miles an hour. This way, says Gongwer, you can swim all day with it; it saves your strength. This is the point. You don't use your arms, you simply hold them still in the same position you would use in the sidestroke. Your arms don't get tired.

"Your power," says Gongwer, "comes from your legs. That's where your power is. Your leg, butt, stomach, and back muscles are the strongest muscles in your body. That's part of our secret." He himself recently swam with the Aqueon for five hours in the Bahamas in a heavy sea. Says Gongwer, "We have adapted the porpoise tail so it fits a human."

Gongwer, a bronzed Californian, is the president of Innerspace Corporation, a joint venture with Aerojet-General Corporation. In Pasadena, California, Innerspace sells Aqueon by mail. Gongwer is a hydrodynamist specializing in underwater propulsion who has been making designs for underwater military installations for a number of years.

The thrust of the porpoise tail is so great that aboard the Aqueon you can, according to Gongwer, dive without weights for 30 feet or so. You can kick the Aqueon off in an emergency. With a snorkel and face mask you can swim on the surface for hours, staring down meanwhile into the water beneath you.

You can loop a bit of rope around the porpoise tail and tow a swimmer through the water easily with it, conserving your strength or making speed as you do so. Gongwer towed me; the sensation I felt was of rushing through the water. Gongwer demonstrated how powerful a swimmer is with the Aqueon by towing two swimmers with ease. The first man being towed hangs on to the rope loop over the porpoise tail, the second man grasps the ankles of the first.

The Aqueon seems to me to be one of the most useful of the new simple, practical devices that help any man or woman explore the offshore depths over the continental shelf.

Better skin- and scuba-diving equipment is helping shallow-depth explorers these days find the sunken treasures that have eluded men for so long, presumably because they couldn't dive down, stay down, and look for them properly.

One firm, the Real 8 Corporation, near Vero Beach, Florida, in the summer of 1965 found a treasure trove just offshore, beneath 6 to 8 feet of sand and 15 to 30 feet of water—ingots and plates of silver, chunks of silver coins, gold bullion. All this came from Spanish Plate Fleet ships sunk off Cape Canaveral in 1715. The find was Real 8's second in two years from the same sunken treasure fleet. The first—$1.6 million worth of pieces of eight, doubloons, jewelry, silver tableware, delicate Chinese porcelain, plus such less valuable items as cannonballs and sounding leads from Spanish galleons—was exhibited in the National Geographic Society's new Hall of Science and Exploration in Washington, D.C. "The twentieth century's richest find of sunken Spanish treasure," the Society called it. It was also the world's greatest find of sunken wealth since 1687, when Sir William Phips made a similar treasure discovery in the West Indies off Haiti.

Kip Wagner, a Florida housebuilder turned treasure hunter, was the man who found the treasure. He named his company Real 8— from *ocho réales,* Spanish for a piece of eight. Said Wagner, "I spent 18 years in research. I had a crew of hard-working divers and 3 boats crammed with gear. And, above all, I had phenomenal luck."

The story of Kip Wagner's treasure was begun and ended by hurricanes. A hurricane in 1715 off Cape Canaveral caught a Spanish treasure fleet out of Havana, pounded it to splinters on nearby jagged coral reefs, sank 10 of its 11 ships, drowned a thousand seamen and sent $14 million in treasure to Davy Jones's locker—most of it never salvaged. The loss ruined many families in Seville and Cádiz, Spain, and others in Vera Cruz, Mexico, and Cartagena, Colombia.

After another hurricane almost 250 years later, Wagner, combing the sand near Sebastian Beach in Florida found some silver pieces of eight. Next he found, nearby in spiky palmetto scrub, a large, crudely shaped diamond. Excited now, he looked down into the sea from a light plane and spotted a row of dark objects—they were cannons. He hired divers who went to work offshore, some-times in heavy seas and murky, surging waters where a visibility of 10 inches is good. A magnetometer and other metal detectors soon located metal. Then more coins were found, many in sea-blackened 60-pound clumps. There were shiny, almost new, pieces of eight in their centers. Then Wagner's divers with a water jet one day uncovered a carpet, the National Geographic Society says, of more than 1,000 gold doubloons. The most valuable single object yet retrieved is a gold chain of 2,176 handmade links, each faceted with rosettes. It is worth $50,000.

Another sunken hull of a Spanish treasure ship, a galleon found off Bermuda in 1963, is of great historical interest. It is thought by the Smithsonian Institution to be the earliest identifiable shipwreck found so far in the Western Hemisphere. From coins around the wreck, the hull appears to date from 1565, only three-quarters of a century after Columbus sailed to America. An impression made in the coral by a coin shows the titles of Ferdinand and Isabella, who sponsored Columbus.

I talked with Mendel L. Peterson, chairman of the Department of Armed Forces History at the Smithsonian, who is himself a diver. Going down to sunken treasure ships, he finds objects that made history: a small Spanish ax, for instance, probably used by boarding parties, and also cobblestones for ballast, used in the 1700's to offset the heavy 80-foot masts of sailing vessels. This is why the Gulf of Mexico and the Caribbean are ringed today with port towns that have cobblestone streets.

For three centuries Spain shipped treasure around Florida, to take advantage of the five-knot Gulf Stream there, and in that time Spanish ships were attacked by Frenchmen, Englishmen, Dutchmen, and pirates as well as by hurricanes. The pirates of the West Indies established their own "nations" and flew their own flags: a skull and crossbones on a black field, or a dancing skeleton, perhaps holding a drink in one hand, a sword in the other. The Florida

Straits, Mr. Peterson says, became for the Spaniards "almost a deathtrap."

As a result, Mr. Peterson told me, the Florida Keys "are one of the richest areas in the world" for wrecks.

There are two principal ways to find a sunken wreck, he explained. One way is to spot it as you cruise among the keys, or as you fly above them. You can sometimes look down and see coral-covered cannons. The other way is to find the location of a wreck from an old manuscript.

The Library of Congress not long ago published a list of manuscripts you may want to pore over—the treasure maps and charts in its collection. This list costs thirty cents. It tells, whenever possible, where the maps and charts can be purchased.

When and if you find anything heavy to lift on the sea bottom, you can use another one of today's new undersea tools to do the work. This is a balloon that folds down into a bundle about the size of those plastic raincoats you slip into your purse or pocket. You hook it onto whatever you want to lift, and blow it up with your mouthpiece or with a spare tank. It now functions as a balloon. Its manufacturer, Hypro Diving of Cambridge, Massachusetts, says it can lift anchors, motors, wreckage, cannons, timbers, bags full of fish or shellfish, pieces of coral, rock or plant specimens, and archaeological treasures. It is available in various lifting capacities of from 100 to 1,000 pounds.

Among other new devices for offshore explorers there are propeller-driven sleds that haul scuba divers. They are called by Jacques-Yves Cousteau "the poor man's bathyscaphe." Aerojet-General has a device called Aquaped that a swimmer pedals and thus turns a propeller behind his feet, driving himself through the water.

The same company offers the Mini-Sub. This is a submarinelike underwater vehicle designed to carry divers from place to place and so conserve their strength. But because the hull of the Mini-Sub is open to the sea, the divers are wet (not inside a dry waterproof hull), and they must have breathing apparatus. This Aerojet program of underwater propulsion grew out of efforts to develop new equipment for the underwater demolition teams of the Navy's frogmen.

Jim Stubstad, project manager for Mini-Sub, tells what it's like to ride one of the open-to-the-sea vehicles. "The water keeps you in a semiweightless state, it's silent as a tomb, and the world just seems to slip slowly beneath you. No traffic jams, smog, telephones, or old TV movies, either. You can really get away from it all."

The *National Fisherman–Maine Coast Fisherman,* a national fisheries monthly, reported not long ago that the Detroit Testing Laboratory, Inc., planned one of the most practical of all submersible vehicles so far, the *Trident.* The *Trident,* designed by Charles R. Meldrum, an aeronautical engineer, like the Mini-Sub, is not watertight. Her passengers must use underwater breathing apparatus and draw upon built-in air reserves. When they leave *Trident,* which they can do on the sea floor, they use portable air tanks. The *Trident* will be able to travel underwater at 15 to 18 knots, and her range will be up to 100 miles at a depth to 300 feet—a superb speed and range for any scuba diver's vehicle.

Besides finding sunken treasure, many other surprising sea adventures may take place close to shore. As an example, take the experience of Dr. Lionel A. Walford, director of the Sandy Hook (New Jersey) Marine Laboratories of the Bureau of Sport Fisheries and Wildlife of the Department of the Interior. On July 18, 1963, he and six other scientists, aboard the 85-foot research vessel *Challenger* just off the New Jersey coast, beheld a long, thin sea monster. It looked like a sea serpent. Dr. Walford said it was 40 to 50 feet long, and from 5 to 7 inches in diameter. "It was silvery and translucent," Dr. Walford told me, "with golden spots along the side. The forepart of the animal was under the boat and hence beyond our range of vision. We confirmed identification of the animal from published descriptions and figures as an oarfish, *Rega-*

lecus glesne. Ours was at least 10 feet longer than the largest specimen recorded."

The oarfish, or ribbonfish, for years has been thought to be one of the beasts that gives rise to tales of the sea serpent. It is a fish of the far oceans and of the great ocean abyss. Nobody knows why, occasionally, it is spotted on the surface—perhaps because it is injured or dying. Osmond P. Breland of the University of Texas, who records the measurements of unusual specimens of the animal kingdom, says the longest oarfish ever measured was about 20 feet long. Dr. Walford's long ribbonfish will make an interesting addition to Dr. Breland's records. And to see it Dr. Walford did not have to make a long trip to midocean; he was just a few miles, in fact, from New York City.

Much is yet to be learned about the creatures of the sea. There was the case of the man who saw an octopus using a tool—an event that, if not eyewitnessed, would not be believed. "Once I remember watching an octopus lie in wait for some time beside the closed shell of a large clam," Albro Gaul writes in *The Wonderful World of the Seashore.* "The moment the bivalve finally opened its shell, the octopus quickly thrust a stone between the clamshells with one of its eight arms, preventing the clamshell from closing again, and laying its occupant open to the octopus' attack. This performance seemed to show not only something of the acuity of the octopus' vision, but also its intelligence in using tools for getting its food."

Skin and scuba divers are already busy exploring for minerals from the edge of the shore on outward. The most successful mining of the sea to date is for oil, natural gas, and sulfur from beneath the continental shelves just offshore. Phosphorite for fertilizer also is obtained offshore. Says H. D. Hess, of the Marine Technology Center of the U.S. Bureau of Mines at Tiburon, California: "Present sea-floor mining operations are in relatively shallow waters of the continental shelf, at depths less than 400 feet." Writing in the August 1965 *Engineering and Mining Journal* (McGraw-Hill),

Mr. Hess lists, as coming from the shallow seabed in recent years, iron, tin, gold, sulfur, coal, shell, sand, and gravel.

"Marine beaches," he writes, "may contain accumulations of gold, silver, platinum, diamonds, and tin mineral in addition to heavy-mineral concentrations of magnetite, chromite, monazite, ilmenite, zircon, and rutile. Columbium, tantalum, tungsten, uranium, thorium, and rare-earth minerals may also be abundant in beach sands that adjoin favorable metallogenic (containing ore deposits) areas. Certain light minerals such as calcium carbonate (shells) and silica sand can also occur in significant concentrations."

Southern Oregon beaches, Mr. Hess says, may contain gold, silver, platinum, and heavy minerals. There is magnetite near Redondo Beach, California. Off the Alaskan coast, Mr. Hess says, there are "promising heavy-mineral sand deposits . . . containing tin, mercury, tungsten, columbium-tantalum, uranium, thorium, and rare earths." Tin also can be found off Alaska.

"Gold was discovered," says Mr. Hess, "on the beaches of Norton Sound, Alaska, in 1898, and triggered a large gold rush. The following year, gold was found in an ancient beach deposit 70 feet above sea level. More recently a gold-bearing submerged beach was discovered 19 feet below sea level off the coast of Nome, and is responsible for the current surge in exploration activity now in progress in the Norton Sound area." As this book was written, the Auric Offshore Mining Company was attempting to recover gold in the sea about 50 miles east of Nome. "All evidence," writes Mr. Hess, "indicates that the offshore sands in Norton Sound may be as rich or richer than the most famous gold-producing beach of all times, the Nome gold coast, which yielded $100 million in gold."

Gold is reported offshore in many regions of the world, such as Nova Scotia, Canada's Northwest Territories, Panama, Chile, and Turkey. One of the richest deposits is off the delta of the Lena River in Russia, with a content of gold worth about $250 per cubic yard. The *Engineering and Mining Journal* calls it "one of the most amazing marine gold deposits ever discovered." The discoverer was the late Herbert Hoover, who spent many months in Russia after World War I.

Working alone, one man off Alaska recently struck it rich. In the Stephens Passage area at Windham Bay, using a suction dredge, he was reported in an engineering journal to have recovered $42,000 in gold during 8 months—and this in water limited to 40 feet in depth. There is no reason to believe that the gold gets less as the water gets deeper. It is there, presumably, waiting for men to go down into the depths and obtain it. "The vast storehouse of virgin mineral wealth in the world's last new mining frontier," says Mr. Hess, "remains essentially untouched."

The World's Best Fisherman
Captures Offshore Monsters

"IF YOUR BOY plays hooky to go fishing," says Bill Gray, "encourage him."

Captain William B. Gray, 75, played hooky until he was 16 years old. He has since been called, more than once, "the world's best fisherman." For the last 50 years he has been bringing back alive from the continental shelf and the open sea rare fishes—giant sharks, disk-shaped sunfishes 8 feet in diameter, porpoises that think, and creatures completely unknown, never seen before by man. He is perhaps the greatest collector of live sea animals in history. As director of collections and exhibits at the Miami (Florida) Seaquarium, he has personally captured for this living museum of the sea many of its ten thousand exhibits—more than you can see at any other aquarium on earth.

There is no simpler way to get a glimpse of the continental shelf and the shallow depths of the sea than to visit the aquariums of the United States, Canada, or abroad. Many aquariums, like the Miami Seaquarium, which opened in 1955, have been built since World War II. Many of their exhibits are the only one of their kind in the world.

Some of today's aquariums and what they show you:

The John G. Shedd Aquarium in Chicago, opened in 1930, shows a 40-foot swamp complete with turtles, fish, and other swamp dwellers. The postwar New York Aquarium at Coney Island, whose

The Navy's new *Alvin* (shown here) and other deep-diving submarines are first craft in history that can carry men to explore the great depths. *Alvin* was first sub to dive over a mile. Her crew gazes through ports.

Alvin's big propeller turns side to side to steer her. Men aboard her, over half a mile down, cruised just above Mediterranean sea bottom and actually found a missing U.S. H-bomb—an object only twelve feet long.

J. Louis Reynolds' *Aluminaut* is first submarine able to dive three miles. When she went down 6,250 feet, she broke *Alvin*'s record. She also helped look for H-bomb.

Deep Jeep is new Navy two-man vehicle that joined H-bomb search. With floodlights, men aboard her explore almost unknown layer of sea 2,000 feet down.

Jon Lindbergh, son of aviator Charles A. Lindbergh, enters cockpit of *Cubmarine*. Lindbergh and *Cubmarine* sought H-bomb, today explore as far as 600 feet down.

Unmanned deep-diving robot called CURV normally recovers research torpedoes for Navy. On Mediterranean bottom, H-bomb was found with parachute attached. CURV inserted grappling hooks into parachute's risers. Then H-bomb was recovered.

William Ogg Rainnie, Jr., a graduate of Naval Academy and submarine fleet, is chief pilot of *Alvin*.

With H-bomb found, *Alvin* (top) and *Aluminaut* met at bomb site, took turns guarding bomb lest it vanish. From *London Daily Express*.

Another new deep-diving vehicle is Navy's *Moray*. She submerges 6,000 feet. Diver is taking movies.

Jacques-Yves Cousteau of France in 1942 developed aqualung to lead way for men into the depths. In 1966 his new *Deepstar 4000* (shown here) dived 4,000 feet.

Dawn of a new era: Science explores the depths. On May 11, 1966, a flag flutters in the currents 4,000 feet down 15 miles southwest of Point Loma, California. It has just been planted by Cousteau and Westinghouse's *Deepstar 4000,* on the new submersible's first deep dive. The three men in the sub brought up some of the long-armed brittle starfish and round sea urchins shown here.

Jacques-Yves Cousteau designed diving saucer, first midget submarine to make regularly scheduled trips to bottom of sea: 400 in all, 125 off California. From now on, science will explore inner space—the depths of the sea—in a program that may produce more adventure, knowledge, and wealth than space travel.

What has been called the greatest natural-history discovery of recent years came out of the sea: The coelacanth, a prehistoric fish believed extinct for 70 million years, was found thriving off South Africa.

What may be a breakthrough for men in the sea: Waldemar Ayres breathes, through tube, oxygen he gets from seawater through a fine sieve he invented. If a man can breathe the sea, he can stay down.

This strange fish, dragging trawl (part of itself) behind, is one of the rarest animals on earth. The tiny black fish has been caught—just once—by University of Miami.

What animal made mysterious swirling tracks on floor of abyss? For years, no one knew. Then Columbia-Cambridge universities' camera caught the animal at 15,534 feet: a three-foot-long acorn worm.

From 4,000 feet beneath sargasso sea comes the *Gonostomatid.*
Teeth are needle-sharp. Light organs line lower edge of side.
Sausage below throat is parasite.

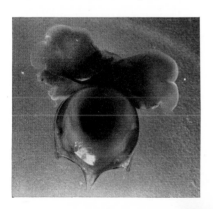

Pteropod, winged snail, flutters
through ocean in the manner of a
moth. *William M. Stephens photos.*

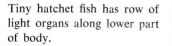

Tiny hatchet fish has row of
light organs along lower part
of body.

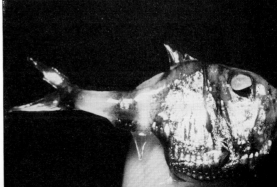

Nuclear submarines map ocean depths (with sound); their men watch water around them (with TV cameras); they have sailed beneath Arctic ice to North Pole. Here are *Skate* and *Seadragon* on top of the world.

Way to the depths is opened from surface ships by Columbia University's Maurice Ewing. His men sampled bottom rocks (by trawls), sediment (by corers), depths (by sound), and found beneath the sea earth's greatest mountain range and deepest canyons.

Shallow depths just offshore are explored with a wooden device called Aqueon that multiplies a swimmer's or diver's power. When Jean Gongwer kicks, framework shoots her through water. Board in her hands takes her up or down, like elevator on airplane.

Drill on giant floating platform will drill Mohole through earth's crust to sample what's inside. This is a model; pontoons on actual platform will be size of submarines. Mohole will be near Hawaii.

In 1963 many surface vessels probed the depths trying to find the sunken submarine *Thresher.* After a month of searching, *Atlantis II* photographed debris on bottom. Then the *Robert D. Conrad,* directed by J. Lamar Worzel, hauled up fifteen packages of Neoprene "O" rings (shown here) used by Navy ships.

Search for *Thresher* narrowed to ocean-floor area 800 yards long by 200 wide. After two months of searching, *Conrad* photographed a Navy air bottle on bottom. Dark objects are part of camera lighting system.

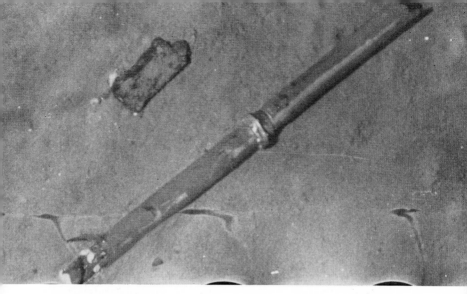

Piece of pipe similar to that used in construction of naval ships was photographed by *Conrad*. As search area now was small, and bottom currents were found tolerable, it was decided to send men down to look.

Only device in 1963 that could take eyewitnesses down to *Thresher*-search-area's 8,400-foot depth was bathyscaphe *Trieste*. Here two men ride in sphere. Today's deep-diving fleet did not exist in 1963.

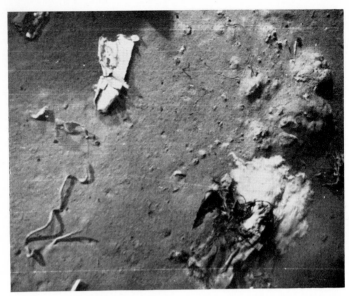

In *Trieste* between late June and late August 1963 Lt. Comdr. Donald L. Keach made ten dives. He saw and photographed rock-wool insulation of a type used in all U.S. Navy submarines.

Thresher was still unlocated, so search went on; then Keach discovered more debris. He found bottom "like an automobile junkyard." He photographed section of sonar dome from *Thresher* (shown here).

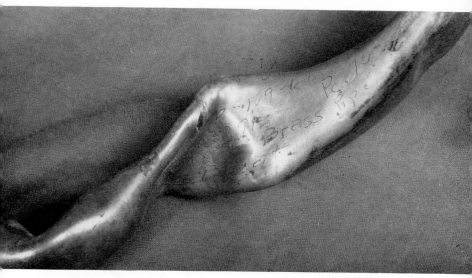

Keach tried *Trieste*'s mechanical arm to bring up a piece of *Thresher*. "I've never been able to pick up anything before—not even a starfish," he said. He retrieved brass pipe with *Thresher*'s number, 593.

Not till 1964 did *Mizar,* from surface, with Chester L. Buchanan operating much of her equipment, photograph *Thresher*'s sail (shown here), showing No. 593, and after-portion of hull. *Thresher* had been found.

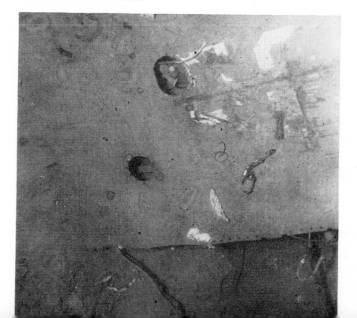

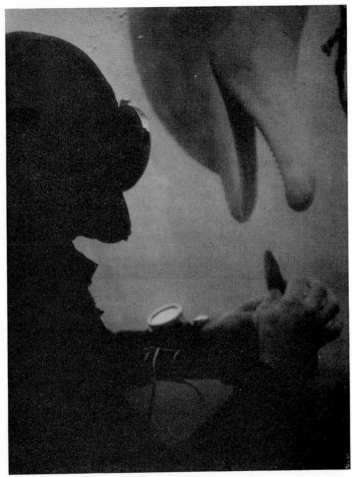

Tuffy the porpoise, here 80 feet down with Navy Diver John Reaves of Sealab II, carried messages and tools to Navy men living beneath the sea in Sealab II. Porpoises show promise of understanding instructions and becoming the No. 1 assistant to man as man moves into and explores a far huger realm than the land surface: the depths of the sea.

director is Dr. Ross R. Nigrelli, has shown white whales flown in from Alaska. Former director Christopher W. Coates made it the world's center of research on the electric eel. The Steinhart Aquarium in San Francisco (completed in 1923, renovated in 1963) has bred and reared difficult species in captivity. The National Aquarium in the Commerce Building, Washington, D.C. (today freshwater fishes, reptiles, amphibians) is to be relocated in a multimillion-dollar home. The T. Wayland Vaughn aquarium-museum of the Scripps Institution of Oceanography, San Diego, displays albacores, sea slugs, deep-water fluorescent organisms, rare jawfish, and (just caught) black sea horses. The Cleveland, Ohio, aquarium displays tropical fish and Atlantic harbor seals plus an arapaima, a great South American river fish that Captain Gray wants to catch. The James R. Record Aquarium, Fort Worth, Texas, shows pink boutus (fresh-water porpoises) from the Amazon. The Toledo, Ohio, aquarium holds the paddlefish. Marine Studios (also called Marineland) near St. Augustine, Florida, which opened in 1937, has performing porpoises, groupers, and reef fishes. Marineland of the Pacific, near Los Angeles, opened in 1954. It actually has tamed and trained pilot whales. The Gulfarium, Ft. Walton Beach, Florida, has glass panels all the way down to the bottom of one tank that make you feel you are walking on the bottom of the sea. Vancouver, Canada, has the Vancouver Public Aquarium, which has an almost endless collection of starfish and octopuses you can shake hands with, and in 1962 helped the Canadian Department of Fisheries capture a two-ton basking shark. This is the second-biggest shark in the sea, smaller only than the whale shark (Chapter 13).

One of the most famous aquariums, that of Prince Albert of Monaco, opened in 1910. In 1950 it introduced something many aquariums have since copied: vanishing sidewall tanks. The sidewalls flare outward; to a visitor in front of a tank the walls seem to disappear, and thus the tanks seem much huger than they are, and fish appear as if in the sea. At the Bergen, Norway, aquarium, the specimens are grouped by families and species. At Munich, Germany, the fish are grouped geographically. The Mito aquarium, near Tokyo, Japan, has kept in captivity the 30-foot piked whale. This is a rorqual, as is the biggest whale of all, the blue or sulfur-bottom. The Berlin, Germany, and Plymouth, England, aquariums have both been rebuilt since World War II. At Naples, Italy, where the oldest marine biological station in the world opened in 1874, there are exhibits for the public and small tanks where scientists can observe specimens. The Brighton, England, aquarium is one that has made a name for itself by keeping octopuses—but not without disaster. One night an octopus operated a valve, let all the water out of a tank, and caused a lot of octopuses to die before morning.

Aquariums contribute a great deal to science. The Miami Sea-quarium has compiled one of the world's largest collections of color slides of tropical fish and animals. It will soon publish an identification guide to them. It also makes educational filmstrips and 16-millimeter movies.

Burton Clark, general manager of the Miami Seaquarium and a consultant to the National Aquarium, thinks that aquariums are largely responsible for support for bills in Congress to support oceanographic research. Clark points out that aquariums give the public a glimpse of the world beneath the sea. "We have opened to all," he says, "a world that no human beings except divers could enjoy before."

Another place to visit to explore the underwater world is the John Pennekamp Coral Reef State Park off Florida's west coast.

Captain Gray and the Miami Seaquarium plan a dream expedition for the future. It will be a 6,000-mile round trip to the Galá-pagos Islands, located on the equator 600 miles from Ecuador in the Pacific. Here the expedition will go after dragons, golden groupers, jeweled fishlets (tropical fish), penguins, flightless cor-morants and—maybe—a killer whale.

The dragons include the marine iguanas (lizards) of the Galá-pagos, the only seagoing iguanas in the world. Captain Gray plans to bring back and cultivate the particular seaweed they eat. The dragons also include the giant lava (land) iguanas of the Galá-pagos.

"I won't say for sure we will bring back a killer whale," says Captain Gray, "but we may catch a young one. I know they are there." Captain Gray has been to the Galápagos three times before.

The black-and-white killer whale, 30 feet long (males), or 15 feet long (females), with a 6-foot-high dorsal fin sticking up like a submarine's conning tower, has never been kept successfully in captivity. This is, however, being attempted: A 4-ton, 22-foot killer was netted in the Pacific in July 1965, and towed inside a floating pen to Seattle for display there. It is the only killer whale in captivity. As it was towed in, Boeing Company scientists listened to the talk between it and killers outside the pen. There were squeals and chirps and other signals—excited communication in individual voices of whales.

Asked what the killer whale likes to eat, Captain Gray replied, "People!"

This at once raises the question of what—or whom—Captain Gray intends to feed a killer if he ever gets one into the Seaquarium's 80-foot-diameter main tank. But perhaps the killer's reputation as a man-eater is exaggerated.

There were stories, not long after 1900, that suggested the killer might threaten a man, or his dogs. On an Antarctic expedition, some of the sled dogs were standing on an ice floe when killers dived beneath the floe, rammed it, and shattered it. The dogs scampered away—barely. On Robert Falcon Scott's 1911–12 expedition to the Antarctic, H. G. Ponting, a photographer, was on an ice floe when killers broke up the floe. He too barely escaped. But divers in Morocco say that the killer swims around men and away from them, just as does its cousin, the porpoise.

The killer is, without question, the fiercest meat-eating animal on land or sea. It attacks even the 150-ton blue whale. Even if it does not consume men, what the killer does gulp down poses a big enough feeding problem for the Seaquarium. Inside one killer's stomach there were found 13 complete porpoises and 14 seals. A fifteenth seal was on its way down the killer's throat.

The biggest fish is not always the most important one for Captain Gray to catch. On one trip into the Pacific, Captain Gray caught a baby sailfish five inches long. It was the first baby sailfish ever taken. Some years ago, on the George Vanderbilt Expedition to mid-Pacific, he helped bring back 50,000 specimens, 62 of them new species and 43 new subspecies. You can see some of these today in the Vanderbilt Museum on Long Island, New York. A number of newly identified fish have been named for Captain Gray.

Porpoises rather than rarer fish are what have brought fame to Captain Gray and the Miami Seaquarium. There is Sparkle, for instance. Sparkle, the prima donna of the Seaquarium's porpoise show, has been taught to play basketball and sing duets by her trainer, Adolf Frohn, who was the first professor of porpoisology on earth (that is, the first man to train porpoises). There is also Clown, who counts up to three. Upon request, as taught by her trainer, Jimmy Kline, Clown puts three oranges into a tub in the water, balances the tub on her head, then leaps into the air so Kline can grab the tub off her head.

There was Carolina Snowball, who died in 1965, 400 pounds in weight and 8 feet long, the only known white porpoise in the world. Her teeth were ebony-black. A few years ago Carolina Snowball was rumored to be living off the coast of South Carolina. Out went Captain Gray and Captain Emil Hanson in the Seaquarium's collecting ship. They sighted the white (really pale-pink) porpoise. They fenced her in, they thought. She jumped over the net. They tried again. She escaped under the net. Altogether Snowball frustrated Captain Gray for 58 days. But, along with a normally colored gray son, she finally was captured and taken to the Seaquarium. There she had her own attendant, a suntanned Florida bathing beauty who swam with her, played with her, and fed her. Captain Gray believed Carolina Snowball and her little boy were happy at the Seaquarium. "She was," he says, "beautiful, friendly, kind, and smart."

Captain Gray not long ago delivered porpoises to an aquarium in Barcelona, Spain. He started transporting them in rubber tanks via ship. The tanks leaked. So he had to pen his porpoises in the ship's swimming pool while the tanks were being repaired. The passengers liked the porpoises so much that they let the porpoises stay in the pool all the way across the ocean.

At the Miami Seaquarium porpoises leap through hoops, bowl, and otherwise entertain visitors. Other marine animals add to the show. Sharks cruise in a large, doughnut-shaped channel. Sharks have trouble adjusting to rectangular tanks. Sea horses, silvery lookdowns (a fish), and other small fish live in 26 corridor tanks around the three-story main tank. Around the bottom of the main tank there are 150 show windows where you can stand as though you were at the bottom of the sea and look up at sawfish, manta rays, nurse sharks, sea turtles, groupers, moray eels, and porpoises.

But the most famous of all the Seaquarium's exhibits is the porpoise known as Flipper. He is the star provided by Ivan Tors Studios for the half-hour show on NBC-TV, a show made at the Seaquarium. Flipper is now so thoroughly trained he swims onto a foam rubber blanket so that he can be transported to filming locales. This is unusual and almost incredible for a wild animal since Flipper is risking his life. He would die if his friends did not help him get back into the water. Flipper in real life is not what you might expect. He is really a lady porpoise named Susie.

PART
III

Man Probes the Abyss

CHAPTER
8

*A Submarine Is Built
to Dive Three Miles*

A SUBMARINE capable of descending 15,000 feet, or almost 3 miles, today sails the seas. This means she can explore 60 percent of the ocean floor—almost all of it unseen by man up to now.

She can reach the bottom of most of the abyss—the nine-tenths of the ocean beyond the continental shelf.

She is J. Louis Reynolds' *Aluminaut.*

A $3-million craft, she has reached 6,250 feet down on one trial dive (250 feet deeper than the *Alvin* went), has submerged 2,700 feet down in another, and has stayed down for 33 hours—the record length of time of submersion for a deep-diving or research submarine. She has been deeper than any other submarine ever, and she has the capability to go much deeper still.

The 6,250-foot dive—almost a mile and a quarter deep, and 8 hours long—was made by the *Aluminaut* November 11, 1965, off Great Abaco Island in the Bahamas. She dived fast—more than 100 feet a minute—to demonstrate she could dive rapidly and thus have more time to spend on the ocean floor. Men in the *Aluminaut* have found sunken ships, encountered rare deep-sea fish, and have observed porpoises at depths below 600 feet. That's 200 feet deeper than porpoises previously had been known to go.

The *Aluminaut*'s crew also has seen a "snowstorm" of living and dead organisms swirling past her windows. In total blackness, 2,500 feet down, her men watched a parade of luminescent animals brighten the depths. "We can see and easily photograph anything 50 to 60 feet ahead of us, even at those dark depths," the *Aluminaut*'s captain, Robert E. Serfass, says.

The *Aluminaut* is 50 feet 11 inches long, or about as long as the biggest fish in the sea, the whale shark; somewhat shorter than the sperm whale; and slightly longer than the California gray whale, an ocean animal that thousands see every year as it swims along the Pacific coast. As one of the important purposes of deep-diving submarines is to enable eyewitnesses to observe directly concentrations of marine life, men aboard the *Aluminaut* may themselves see, through her viewing ports, all of these sea animals and others besides. It sounds farfetched, but men aboard the *Aluminaut* might one day help point the way toward what some scientists think will come in the future: pods of whales herded by whaleboys (undersea cowboys) riding in small submarines.

The *Aluminaut*'s orange-and-blue aluminum hull is 6½ inches thick. Including her hull thickness, the *Aluminaut* is 8 feet 1 inch in diameter. Her inside diameter is 7 feet. The crew has room to walk around. The crew, usually two or three men, was expanded for the 2,700-foot dive and included Skipper Serfass of San Diego, California; Art Markel, a Naval Academy graduate of the class of 1948; Robert H. Canary, Groton, Connecticut; Alfred L. Rutherford, Montville, Connecticut; James J. Cooney, Philadelphia; and Horace D. Barnett of Groton, Connecticut. Dr. T. Robert Kendall, an oceanographer from the University of Hawaii, was aboard *Aluminaut*'s tender. On the 6,250-foot dive, D. K. Breese of Miami replaced Barnett.

When *Aluminaut* reaches her 15,000-foot depth, her length will be reduced one inch by the pressure of the sea, and her diameter will be one-tenth of an inch less than it is on the surface.

If marine zoologists aboard the *Aluminaut* ever do set out to watch whales in the depths—something scientists never have done and want badly to do—they would have an interesting time of it. The *Aluminaut* could easily outdive the California gray whale, which goes down only to about 300 feet. The sperm whale would be a problem of a different nature. American whalers once pursued the sperm in great numbers to obtain its oil for lamps, and knew from the way a harpoon line sizzled out when a sperm was on the end of one that it dived fast and deep. Not till we began to haul up dead sperms entangled in cables on the bottom did we learn how deep. Dr. Bruce Heezen of Columbia University's Lamont Geological Observatory is the custodian of the records. He has collected accounts of 14 sperm whales ensnarled in cables—half of them 3,000 feet or more down. The deepest was 3,720 feet, or seven-tenths of a mile down. "It is virtually certain," says C. P. Idyll, "that among diving animals they are unexcelled." It is possible the sperm whale in each case mistook the cable for the arm of an octopus or of a giant squid and sought to do battle with the beast it thought it saw. In almost every case the cable was wrapped around the sperm whale's jaws.

The *Aluminaut* would have trouble keeping up with either the sperm whale or the 100-foot-long or longer blue or sulfur-bottom whale, the hugest beast in the oceans and the biggest animal that ever lived on earth, so far as men can tell—even larger than the largest dinosaurs. Either could pull away from the *Aluminaut,* which is driven by batteries at up to 3.8 knots. On her 33-hour trip submerged, she traveled at up to 3.5 knots.

The sperm's cruising speed of 4 knots can be increased to 12 knots if the sperm feels uneasy, as it might with a submarine chasing it. The blue whale's cruising speed of 10 knots is enough itself to rapidly outdistance the *Aluminaut;* when pressed, the blue whale can make 22 knots, the speed of an ocean liner. Two 5-horsepower direct-current electric motors drive the *Aluminaut*'s twin screws. This is exactly one-fiftieth of the incredible 500 horsepower the blue whale develops when 20 tons of muscles waggle the end of its spine and thus push it along at that 22-knot speed.

The *Aluminaut* at 75 tons is about equal in weight to the biggest sperm, which weighed 70 tons (this record sperm was 70 feet in length). As the sperm whale used to fight and overturn whalers' boats, and even on one occasion used its great head (one-third of its body length) to crush the timbers of a Nantucket whaling ship and sink her, so the sperm whale might attack the *Aluminaut*. The main result probably would be that the submarine's crew would be shaken up. Her men presumably would be more shaken up by the collision with a blue whale. The world's record blue, weighed chunk by chunk aboard a Japanese whaler January 27, 1948, totaled 150 tons, or 300,707 pounds. That's as much as two *Aluminauts,* or two hundred 150-pound men, or 35 adult elephants, or five 70-foot-long brontosaurs. Lt. Col. Walden C. Winston, U.S. Army, who was along on the Japanese whaler, believes that there are larger blue whales in the oceans. Even their year-old babies are large enough. At 50 feet long, they are almost at long as the *Aluminaut*. They are the only known 50-foot-long infants in the world.

There is a record of a great whale, a blue or some other, coming up beneath a motor schooner, apparently to blow, and lifting the ship clear of the water and dumping her on her side.

Either the sperm or the blue whale has more endurance than the *Aluminaut* (or, for that matter any other submarine). Both can keep cruising, except for occasional naps, throughout a lifetime estimated at 25 years. Only Heaven knows how many thousands of miles they travel. The *Aluminaut* covers 80 to 100 miles underwater. On her 33-hour trip, she did 70 miles and crossed the Gulf Stream as she went from the Grand Bahama banks to Miami. The *Aluminaut* can far outlast the whales at remaining submerged. She can normally remain down around 32 hours; she can spend 72 hours submerged in an emergency. Whales breathe air, and must surface frequently to obtain it. The sperm whale, the champion sea mammal at staying down, does so only an hour and a quarter at the longest.

Had the *Aluminaut* been in existence when the *Thresher* sank in 8,400 feet of water, she would have been capable of landing on the bottom near the *Thresher*. Should the *Aluminaut* dive as deep as she can, 15,000 feet, at one particular spot on the Atlantic Ocean 750 miles east of Jacksonville, Florida, she will come upon the only structure man has so far erected almost three miles down in any ocean. This is SNAP-7E, an undersea acoustic beacon 5 feet 4 inches tall. Developed by the Navy for both navigation and research, it is powered by a nuclear generator built by the Martin Company. SNAP-7E has pinged once every 60 seconds since July 1964, when it was installed to enable both surface ships and deeply submerged submarines to find their precise location without the use of shore-based navigational aids. Its nuclear generator is designed to produce about 7 watts of continuous electrical power for at least 2 years. The research in which SNAP-7E is participating has to do with the effects of deep-sea environment on the transmission of sound (pings) over long distances. SNAP-7E was developed under the Atomic Energy Commission's SNAP (Systems for Nuclear Auxiliary Power) program. Other Martin-built SNAP nuclear generators for the AEC provide power for space satellites; for navigational aids on offshore oil and gas platforms in the Gulf of Mexico; for a navigational buoy and lighthouse in Chesapeake Bay; and for remote weather buoys far at sea—floating platforms automatically broadcasting wind, wave, temperature, and barometer readings from the Arctic, the Antarctic, the Gulf of Mexico, and the Atlantic.

The *Aluminaut* has two 9-foot-long robot arms, and so on the sea floor, from 12,000 to 15,000 feet down, she can pick up some of the valuable manganese, nickel, and cobalt nodules that, Maurice Ewing says, are just about the commonest objects all over the ocean bottom. She can help sample the ocean bed which, according to J. Louis Reynolds, contains enough aluminum and copper for a million years at the rate at which men use those metals now.

The *Aluminaut* started as an idea in the minds of two men. During World War II, in 1942, Mr. Reynolds, an aluminum executive, was thinking about developing aluminum underseas ships for cargo transportation. The other man was Dr. Edward Wenk, Jr., now Chief of the Science Policy Research Division, Legislative Reference Service, Library of Congress. At the Navy's David Taylor Model Basin, Dr. Wenk pondered the possibility of a deep-diving submarine. At the Southwest Research Institute, San Antonio, Texas, he had a chance to study the construction of hulls that would withstand the pressures at great depths (up to 10,000 pounds per square inch at 22,000 feet). A Southwest Research Institute report for the National Academy of Sciences–National Research Council showed that such submarine hulls could be built with a variety of materials, among them aluminum. By 1959, feasibility studies had shown that high-strength aluminum alloy could do the job. It is used in *Aluminaut*.

The *Aluminaut* was built for Reynolds International, Inc., by a number of companies. The Electric Boat Division of General Dynamics completed her. The *Aluminaut*'s keel, two ballast tanks, and stern structure were manufactured at Bliss-Portland of South Portland, Maine. Next came tests at sea. In Long Island Sound her stability, maneuverability, and handling characteristics were checked out. She went on to Miami, Florida. Her speed runs and endurance dives and her first dives to 15,000 feet were to be made in the Florida-Bahamas area. Here her more sophisticated equipment was tested: advanced sonar systems, television, underwater illumination equipment.

In the summer of 1966, the *Aluminaut* left Miami and took the first eyewitnesses to explore the abyss for mineral wealth. They found it. The *Aluminaut* made a 10-day survey of the 3,000-foot-deep Blake Plateau, a 150-by-100-mile flat underwater Atlantic terrace off North Florida, Georgia, and South Carolina. Her men found a smooth black manganese oxide pavement. "The Gulf Stream currents evidently keep the pavement swept clean of sediment," Arthur L. Markel, her manager, said, "so that it resembles a black-top road. The *Aluminaut* actually rode on her wheels along the deposits just as though she was on a country road." The *Aluminaut* will use two heavy-duty airplane-type wheels to keep her bow off the bottom whenever the seabed is flat or hard enough, or both. She has one wheel under her stern. She raised with her arms a 198-pound specimen of the manganese oxide. It appeared better than minimum standards for commercial grades of manganese oxide. Her crew also recovered phosphate pavement, phosphate nodules, and samples of gray sand.

The abyss which *Aluminaut* will explore is the realm of many mysteries. One of them: What creature makes the "strange mewing sounds, shrieks, and ghostly moans" heard by hydrophones dangled in deep water in Bermuda? Another one: What animal—estimated from its echo to be 11,500 feet deep—made the calls heard by the Woods Hole research ship *Atlantis* near Puerto Rico on March 7, 1949? Whales are not known to dive nearly as deep as this, and crustaceans are not believed to make calls as loud as those the *Atlantis* picked up. The conclusion is that it could only have been some noisy fish of the abyss. But what fish?

Solving such mysteries is only one of the adventures that lie ahead of the *Aluminaut*. She can also measure temperature, pressure, and salinity of the sea; its forces of gravity and its magnetic characteristics; and its currents. In mid-July 1965 she drifted along for 25 miles at 1,000 feet beneath the Gulf Stream. This demonstrated the feasibility of controlled drift for research operations. She can map the ocean floor with her high-resolution sonar, core the bottom with her arm or claw, sample the sediments, make seismic measurements. She can help lay and repair cables and pipelines and could have precisely placed the Martin Company's nuclear-powered undersea navigation aid. And she can carry eyewitnesses as they follow and study the whale. The *Aluminaut,* the first research submarine with a three-mile diving limit, has her work cut out for her.

We Search Out the Greatest

Canyons and Waves

ENSIGN Paul W. Larsen, the watch officer aboard the *Pioneer,* one moment was gazing from the bridge at the calm Indian Ocean. The next moment it wasn't all calm. In patches it was rough. But only in patches. There was a band of calm water. Then would come a band in which the sea was dancing, the waves were capped with white. Then there was another band of calm, then another stretch of rough water.

The banded sea troubled Ensign Larsen. He had never seen anything like it. Few sailors ever have. There was no storm, there were no high winds, there had been no falling barometer, there was nothing in sight to churn up the sea.

Ensign Larsen's vessel, the U.S. Coast and Geodetic Survey Ship *Pioneer,* is also known as Ocean Survey Ship 31. She is a research vessel that operates entirely on the surface—the kind of ship that, until the 1960's, obtained most of our information about the ocean abyss. The world's fleet of such research ships is bigger than ever nowadays, and constantly at work, as was the *Pioneer* when Ensign Larsen noticed the sea was kicking up.

At that moment the *Pioneer* was cruising off the northern tip of Sumatra, in the Bay of Bengal. She was on a 27,000-mile round-trip voyage from Oakland, California, to the Indian Ocean—the farthest voyage of exploration ever undertaken by any Coast and

Geodetic Survey ship. The trip was also the longest in time for a Coast and Geodetic ship: it lasted six months.

The *Pioneer* was one of 48 ships from 20 nations sent to survey the Indian Ocean, a rarely explored sea that covers one-seventh of the entire globe. She and the other ships, organized as the International Indian Ocean Expedition, were trying to learn more about the fishes of the Indian Ocean, its minerals, its weather, its circulation, its rocks and shoals and other navigational hazards, for the benefit of the whole world but particularly for the benefit of the one-fourth of the world's population that lives around its shores. This population could well consume any protein that would result from finding new fishing grounds. The human body requires protein in diets, and fish are a major source of it. Two new fishing grounds were discovered: one near Africa, one near India.

"I was looking," Ensign Larsen recalled, "for birds or surface disturbances—anything that might increase our knowledge.

"It was a calm watch, a little windy. I saw slick [calm] areas in bands about half a mile wide, very different from the choppy water all around.

"Maybe you've seen the ocean where a swiftly flowing river flows into it—it was like that."

Larsen did what any watch officer does when a puzzling condition appears. He called the skipper, Captain Edward B. Brown.

"I also phoned Lieutenant Ray Moses and the other oceanographers, and they came to the bridge," Larsen said.

Lieutenant Moses shared Larsen's puzzlement at the rough-and-smooth ocean. He consulted one of the *Pioneer*'s new tools to explore the depths: a bathythermograph, an instrument that records temperatures of the sea at various levels.

The bathythermograph showed Lieutenant Moses that beneath the surface the layers of water at different temperatures were not at a constant depth, as in a calm ocean, but were fluctuating in wave form. The waves were moving at 5 knots. They were great waves—up to 270 feet high.

Some of the waves were atop others, some were near the surface, some were as deep as 900 feet down.

The ocean's surface waves generally, the Coast and Geodetic Survey says, are no more than 55 feet high. A wave in a Pacific typhoon, the Navy says, once was measured by a Navy ship, the *Ramapo,* to be 112 feet high—the all-time world's record. Skippers and sailors who have been caught in grim North Atlantic winter storms have asserted they encountered waves around 70 feet high —a possibility in that region, crowded with ships and notoriously violent when stormy.

No man has ever seen 270-foot-high waves. No such waves occur on the surface. But though much higher than surface waves, they are not so fearsome; they have low energy and produce only those small waves on the surface.

The *Pioneer* cruised through—or over—them, Captain Brown reported later, for an hour and a half, or for almost 18 miles. Captain Brown came to this conclusion because the *Pioneer* plowed through alternate calm and rough bands of ocean for that distance. The bands of choppy water on the surface were seen again the next day, June 13. On that day the surface waves reached a height of 7 feet. They stretched from horizon to horizon (30 miles) in bands one-eighth of a mile wide.

Undersea waves, also called internal waves, previously had been known. Some as high as 300 feet had been reported. Rachel Carson mentions them in *The Sea Around Us.* H. U. Sverdrup, Martin W. Johnson, and Richard H. Fleming, in their standard text *The Oceans,* explain the waves as occurring where a thin top layer of water of light density covers heavier water underneath.

Lieutenant Moses thought the waves might have resulted from the joining of the waters of different temperatures of the Andaman Sea and the Bay of Bengal at the point where they were detected. Or the waves might be due to the tidal pull of the sun and the moon. Or to the reflecting edge of the ocean basin.

"In any case," said a spokesman for the Coast and Geodetic

Survey, "there is an abrupt change in the density of the waters as a wave passes a given point. An unsuspecting submarine or similar undersea craft moving from the denser water of a wave to the less dense water between waves could lose buoyancy and descend, much as an airplane does when it hits a so-called air pocket [downdraft], although less precipitously. Could undersea waves have caused the tragic loss of the U.S. atomic submarine *Thresher* in 1963?"

An oceanographer aboard the *Pioneer* considered this a possibility. Said Lieutenant Moses, "It is believed the *Thresher* might have been involved in internal waves."

The *Pioneer*'s undersea waves were different from earlier ones reported, Richard B. Perry of the U.S. Coast and Geodetic Survey Office of Research and Development told me, because of the high ratio of height to length. They were steep. "Most very high internal waves," he said, "are believed to be many miles in length rather than approximately one mile, as was the case here."

The *Pioneer*'s observations were significant, Mr. Perry said, in that she measured the waves in the open sea (this is rare; most internal waves have been measured just offshore) and in that she associated the choppy surface bands with the undersea waves. The surface chop had not previously been explained as caused by internal waves.

"The observations," said Mr. Perry, "emphasize the enormous forces that may be operating under the surface of an apparently calm sea."

The great undersea waves were not the only hazard of the abyss discovered on the 1964 trip of the *Pioneer*.

Also in the Bay of Bengal, her scientists found, by echo sounding, mammoth sea channels carved out of the bottom by what they called rivers of mud.

Other channels in the sea floor have been known for years. There is one right outside New York Harbor, at the mouth of the Hudson River. The sea channels the *Pioneer* found were, like her undersea waves, big and numerous.

The *Pioneer* discovered a sea channel 4 miles wide—4 times wider than the Mississippi River. It was 300 feet deep—6 times as deep as the Mississippi. Said Dr. Robert Dietz, an oceanographer of the U.S. Department of Commerce, of which the Coast and Geodetic Survey is a part: "At some past moment it must have carried a volume of muddy water 25 times greater than the Mississippi.

"Over the years," explained Dr. Dietz, "the many rivers which pour into the Bay of Bengal, including the Ganges, Irrawaddy, and Brahmaputra, deposit their mud on the continental shelves, a connecting link with the ocean bottom which begins at the water's edge. Possibly about once or twice each century, this mud suddenly moves with compelling force from the shelves across the bottom of the sea through these huge channels. What triggers these sudden avalanches of mud at the bottom of the sea is not known.

"But the mud is apparently funneled down submarine channels cut into the steep continental slopes, which link the continental shelves and the ocean bottom, and pours across the almost flat sea floor for hundreds of miles. At some time in the distant past, the mud avalanches cut these enormous channels out of the sea bottom.

"Each time this unusual phenomenon occurs, it fills the sea channels to overflowing with huge, massive, fluid rivers of mud or water. The volume is so great that in overflowing the channels the mud builds its own levees or walls, just as the Mississippi River does on land. These mud rivers run along the bottom of the sea like a flood of mercury."

Dr. Dietz was assisted in studying the sea channels by Dr. Harris B. Stewart, Jr., chief oceanographer of the Coast and Geodetic Survey, and by Dr. Francis P. Shepard of the Scripps Institution of Oceanography. Dr. Dietz said that previously such channels had been attributed to structural faults. "Our study," he said, "definitely established that these channels are not structural faults, that they were caused by rivers of mud, that they represent a complex system rather than the isolated two or three we believed existed before. These sea channels in the Bay of Bengal [altogether the *Pioneer* found 20 of them] represent the greatest network and the greatest display of these unusual features found anywhere so far. This is undoubtedly one of the major discoveries of our expedition."

No man knows, Dr. Dietz continued, how long the mud avalanches that carve the canyons last. "We believe they travel at high speed and their volume is measured in millions of cubic yards of mud," he said. "They represent a truly remarkable phenomenon of the sea."

What would it be like to be caught in one of these undersea mud slides in a submarine? "It is probable," says the Coast and Geodetic Survey, "that no submersible craft could withstand the fury of these undersea rivers."

The network of mud rivers and valleys, a discovery announced in November 1964, was big enough. But the *Pioneer* also located, in the Andaman Sea, a huge split in the ocean's floor. This one was announced April 25, 1965. It is a valley 1,700 miles long (more than the airline distance from Washington, D.C., to Denver, Colorado), and up to 25 miles wide, and is framed on both sides by towering mountain peaks that sometimes break the surface and become islands; Narcondam Island in the Indian Ocean, Sumatra, Java, and Timor are formed by the mountains rising above the sea. The valley extends from these islands in Indonesia (formerly the Dutch East Indies) to about 250 miles northwest of Rangoon, Burma. Its mountains are mostly beneath the sea between Sumatra and Burma, then come out again on land to reach the eastern Himalaya range on the Burma-India border. The oceanographers who mapped the valley by soundings taken aboard the *Pioneer* were marine geologists L. Austin Weeks and Reginald N. Harbison, and geophysicist George Peter.

The great split in the sea bottom is a rift valley. "In essence," the Coast and Geodetic Survey explains, "a rift valley is caused by collapse of the earth between fractures. The Andaman Sea rift valley is similar to that extending down the middle of the Mid-Atlantic Ridge, a mountain range which lies beneath the Atlantic Ocean. The rift valleys in the Atlantic and Indian Oceans resulted from the fracturing of the mountain ranges after the volcanic action died down. Volcanic action caused the earth to rise. When the action subsided, the earth settled and a rift valley was created."

The Andaman rift valley, at its deepest point, is 15,000 feet, or almost three miles, beneath the sea. The valley is part of the volcanic arc that includes Krakatoa, the island that became tragically famous when, in the last century, it was destroyed by volcanic eruption. All but a segment of Krakatoa vanished beneath the surface.

The valley was studied aboard the *Pioneer* through the use of a sub-bottom profiler or sparker. This instrument uses sound waves to penetrate the sediments of the ocean floor. The sound waves are reflected from sediments and rock strata and buried structures in such a manner that their depth and disposition can be determined. The profiler turns its sound images into marks on paper; mapping the Andaman Sea rift, it drew something like a canyon filled with mud.

The sediment in the valley, the sparker indicated, is muck and ooze, more than half a mile deep. It is doubtful, the Coast and Geodetic Survey says, that man will ever tread this valley, "regardless of the equipment he wears." The ooze might be so liquid it would swallow a man or a ship; everything might sink into it.

The *Pioneer* on the same trip found the world's steepest continental slope. Chief Scientist Harris Stewart reported a slope from the island of Ceylon into the Bay of Bengal over 45 degrees steep. United States continental slopes on the average are, in the Atlantic, 7 degrees; in the Pacific, 15 degrees. In a distance of only 18 miles off Ceylon, Stewart says, the sea bottom falls from 180 feet to 12,000 feet.

The *Pioneer*'s scientists also found two submarine canyons off Ceylon. They discovered altogether two dozen uncharted submarine mountains. All have their summits several thousand feet beneath the sea. One is on the shipping route between California and Hawaii. These sea mounts will be shown on future charts—the Coast and Geodetic Survey distributes approximately 30 million charts a year to ships and aviation—and their summits will bounce sonar echoes and provide aids to navigation.

Other sea mounts can be dangerous. In 1960 the Survey found an unknown, unmapped 5,800-foot-high mountain on the floor of the Caribbean Sea that comes to within 90 feet of the surface. That one could wreck a submarine. A great undersea wave could conceivably dash a submarine against such an undersea mountain peak.

En route home the *Pioneer* took corings—samples of the sediment on the sea bottom collected in pipes, called corers—from a number of the deepest places in the sea, the great trenches. She obtained a 13-foot-long core from the Marianas Trench off Guam. It will take years to analyze it. The analysis of the layers of sediment that make up the core will tell something about the history of the earth, its ice ages and the intervals between them, and the story of life upon the earth.

Ensign Paul Larsen, the watch officer who first noticed the mysterious, alternately smooth-and-rough surface of the sea that led to the discovery of the undersea waves, is himself a scuba diver. So Larsen went down to have a look at Invisible Bank, a sea mountain which comes close to the surface. He thus became one of the few undersea mountaineers the world has so far known. He found, he reported, millions of brightly colored tropical fish. Near Borneo he dived to Sea Horse Shoals, which he described as an "untouched coral reef where the underwater visibility was 200 to 300 feet— perfectly clear water," and where he observed a little-known and peculiar form of life. Here he saw great numbers of "tennis balls" —some of them almost bouncing off the bottom. These are alga balls, Harris Stewart says, a sort of soft coral; they feel and look like tennis balls, and are tossed around by the currents. Similar growths are found in the Gulf of Mexico.

Intriguing though the "tennis balls" are, Harris Stewart said, discovery of the undersea waves would probably be considered the most significant event of the expedition. "If you had that kind of wave on the surface," he commented, "ocean commerce would come to a halt." Captain Brown of the *Pioneer* called the gigantic waves the "most interesting" result of the trip.

The Coast and Geodetic Survey began functioning in 1807, when the signature of President Thomas Jefferson made it official, and has been exploring and charting the U.S. coast ever since. Today its activities cover all the oceans. It is the Federal Government's chief civilian oceanographic agency. Its ships are called the Commerce Department's "Little Navy." There are 15, with 5 more now being built. Its ships sail from Seattle, Washington; Oakland, California; St. Petersburg, Florida; Savannah, Georgia, and Norfolk, Virginia.

One C.G.S. vessel, the *Surveyor,* in the summer of 1964 completed a hydrographic survey that demonstrated a breathtaking fact: the Good Friday, 1964, earthquake in Alaska was so powerful that it caused the greatest known uplift of land in history. Much of the ocean floor in the Gulf of Alaska was raised over 30 feet, Rear Admiral H. Arnold Karo, director of the Coast and Geodetic Survey, reported. There was a maximum rise of more than 50 feet in three areas. The greatest uplift in history previously recorded was 47⅓ feet in an 1899 Alaska quake.

The Coast and Geodetic Survey's present plans include studying the Gulf Stream, the wandering current in the ocean that rushes past Florida and eventually heads for Europe, shooting out fingers here and there en route. Cooperating on the Gulf Stream studies are the Weather Bureau, the Massachusetts Institute of Technology, the Woods Hole Oceanographic Institution, the University of Rhode Island, the Lamont Geological Observatory of Columbia University, and the University of Miami. The Coast and Geodetic

Survey is charting the Galveston, Texas, bay in detail for the first time in 30 years. It has set up a research group to study the effects of wind, waves, tides, and currents on U.S. beaches and on the sea floor. Around Florida it is charting sea channels, slopes, and elevations. It operates the Pacific Seismic Sea Wave Warning System, a network of 30 tide stations and 15 seismic stations that warns of the onslaught of those other great waves—the destructive tidal waves, or tsunamis, sometimes 100 feet in height on a beach. The Survey's ships have charted altogether more than 500,000 square miles of the Atlantic, Pacific, and Gulf of Mexico coasts; the turbulent seas off Alaska; the tropical seas around Puerto Rico and Hawaii; the Aleutians; and the mid-Atlantic.

Its recent discoveries have caused the Survey itself to revise its own view of the sea. Writes Raymond Wilcove of the Survey:

> Man has long dreamed of the time when huge submersibles could carry the world's oceangoing commerce below the turbulent surface of the seas, moving swiftly through the still waters of the deep.
>
> The greatest obstacle, presumably, was the development of vessels that would be more economical than surface ships. But now, studies by the U.S. Commerce Department's Coast and Geodetic Survey indicate that strange and perilous phenomena lurking beneath the surface present serious problems that must be taken into account in any undersea operations.
>
> The fact is, our oceans are not simply smooth basins filled with water and fish. They are honeycombed with towering mountain peaks and ranges, lofty plateaus and deep valleys, and cuts in the ocean floor far deeper than the spectacular Grand Canyon of the Colorado. And that's not all. Take those massive underwater waves, a little-understood disturbance of the seas.
>
> These perils, not to mention others that may not yet have been discovered, make clear the necessity for extensive, detailed studies of the ocean, especially along

our coasts, to prepare the way for the undersea commerce of the future.

If the ocean abyss, for centuries considered quiet, harbors instead the greatest waves of all, mud slides on a scale the land dweller can scarcely imagine, plus tall mountains, steep slopes, the world's greatest canyons, and forces that can lift the sea floor itself as much as 30 to 50 feet, what other wonders may the ocean depths hide?

CHAPTER
10

At 8,400 Feet, We
Locate the Thresher

ON APRIL 10, 1963, the 278-foot-long, $45 million U.S.S. *Thresher,* a nuclear antisubmarine submarine, failed to surface while making a deep-diving test 220 miles east of Cape Cod, Massachusetts.

Thresher was one of our latest, smartest ships. She was one of the fastest and the deepest diving of our nuclear submarines. How deep she went was kept a secret for military reasons.

Thresher sank in the open Atlantic in 8,400 feet of sea. All aboard were lost with her: 129 officers, men, and civilian technicians. It was the worst submarine disaster in American history, in peace or war and the first time we had lost a nuclear submarine in nine years of operating them.

Never had anyone tried to look for a wreck at such a depth— 8,400 feet. There was no precedent. Divers had indeed reached the *Andrea Doria,* the Italian passenger liner that sank off Nantucket. But the *Andrea Doria* lies on the continental shelf in less than 200 feet of water.

But the Navy, civilian oceanographers, and some of the latest and most sophisticated oceanographic equipment combined to locate the *Thresher,* as the official U.S. Navy photographs prove. What happened essentially was that sonar from the surface located likely spots on the ocean floor to be examined closely. The sonar showed bulges on the bottom that might be the *Thresher.* Then an

800-pound camera designed by Professor Harold E. Edgerton of the Massachusetts Institute of Technology was lowered to 15 to 30 feet above the bottom. The camera carries two stroboscopic lights (high-speed flash). It is a 35-millimeter camera that exposes 500 frames of film in an hour. Each frame shows an approximately 15-by-20-foot patch of the bottom. On each frame the time and depth are automatically recorded. The Edgerton camera, writes Thomas K. Lineaweaver III in *Sea Frontiers,* proved "indispensable to the search. It changed, in fact, the possibility of finding the *Thresher* into a certainty."

At Eastertime, when *Thresher* went down, the Woods Hole Oceanographic Institution research ship *Atlantis II* was not far away. Woods Hole Director Paul Fye immediately radioed her to join the search. She quickly reached the scene, as did destroyers, submarines, tenders, and all kinds of naval vessels.

Atlantis II from April 11 till May 14, 1963, operated her sonar and lowered her Edgerton camera to likely bumps on the bottom. She got excellent pictures of the ocean floor, and she and other probing ships got photographs of the life 8,400 feet down: squid, skate, the frill shark (a near-prehistoric shark). There were no signs of *Thresher*. On May 14, after her last drifts through the search area, *Atlantis II* headed for a short stay at Woods Hole, on Cape Cod. Alexander Johnston processed the last films from the Edgerton camera. He expected the usual pictures of sea bottom and animals. This time he was surprised. Hundreds of pictures showed a one-tenth-mile-wide strip of sea bottom littered with debris: rags, paper, books, bits of torn cable, and unidentified matter. The first definite clue had been found.

A Navy-Columbia University research ship, the *Robert D. Conrad,* dredged up the first specimen of the debris: packages of Neoprene "O" rings. They proved to be a kind carried by naval vessels. A length of pipe with "593 boat" (*Thresher*'s number) scrawled upon it and part of a battery were also retrieved from the sea floor in 1963.

But no one yet knows *why* she sank. On June 20, 1963, Secretary of the Navy Fred Korth said:

> The Navy believes it most likely that a piping system failure had occurred in one of the *Thresher*'s salt-water systems, probably in the engine room. The enormous pressure of seawater surrounding the submarine subjected her interior to a violent spray of water and progressive flooding. In all probability water affected the electrical circuits and caused loss of power. *Thresher* slowed and began to sink. Within moments she had exceeded her collapse depth and totally flooded. She came to rest on the ocean floor 8,400 feet beneath the surface.

U.S. Coast and Geodetic Survey scientists thought it possible that *Thresher* might have been hit by an undersea wave. *Thresher* went down near Georges Bank, a fishing ground that New England fishing boats use. In *Oceanus,* the Woods Hole magazine, Columbus O'D. Iselin suggested that abnormal conditions near the bank might have caused the disaster. Excess water, forced into the Gulf of Maine by a storm a few days earlier, passing back to the open ocean in the channel between Georges Bank and Brown's Bank, might have formed a vast underwater eddy at the point where it met the normal northeasterly offshore current. This was about where *Thresher* made the deep dive from which she did not surface. The effects of the eddy, combined with internal (undersea) waves generated by the storm, could have forced *Thresher* down and down until the pressure was greater than her hull could stand. If at this moment some malfunction occurred, such as the piping-system failure described by Navy Secretary Korth, the tragedy would have been inevitable.

Not till after much more searching was the *Thresher* found—in depths man previously could not look into. How the job was done is shown in the photographs in the picture section.

CHAPTER
11

/ We Plan to Improve
on Jules Verne

OCEANOGRAPHERS are going to do better than Jules Verne ever dreamed. In 1870, or almost 100 years ago, in his fanciful *Twenty Thousand Leagues Under the Sea,* Verne imagined a handful of men exploring the depths of the sea in a submarine named *Nautilus.*

The White House announced on April 18, 1965, that the United States will build an exploring, deep-diving research submarine that will do far more than Jules Verne's *Nautilus.* The U.S. vessel will be driven by nuclear power and so will be able to go to the bottom, stay there, and prowl the sea floor indefinitely.

Jules Verne described the *Nautilus* as a "long object, spindle-shaped." This will be about the shape of the nuclear exploring submarine. Darrell Garwood, of United Press International, says it will be "something like a cigar-shaped grasshopper." Jules Verne had floodlights illuminate the depths for his submarine crew. So will the American submarine for her crew members. The American craft will have many things of which Jules Verne never dreamed: television cameras and mechanical arms and, for that matter, nuclear power.

Jules Verne's *Nautilus* cruised between 300 and 450 feet beneath the surface. The first nuclear exploring submarine will have the capacity to dive to depths greater than 400 feet. She may—her plans are far from complete—have the capacity to dive very much deeper, and so be able to look over much of the continental slope and some of the abyss.

The nuclear exploring submarine's program, the White House said, "will also permit direct and extended accumulation of commercially useful information on the habits of diverse species of marine life." The Bureau of Commercial Fisheries for some time has wanted a nuclear submarine to locate and follow and point out to fishing vessels schools of fish. The nuclear exploring submarine could do so.

The Navy's Special Projects Office will have overall responsibility for the nuclear exploring submarine, the White House said. The Navy's Bureau of Ships will be responsible for her design, development, and construction. The Atomic Energy Commission's Division of Naval Reactors, headed by Vice Admiral H. G. Rickover, will be responsible for the design, development, and fabrication of the propulsion plant. The Atomic Energy Commission's Knolls Atomic Power Laboratory, Schenectady, New York, will develop the nuclear reactor plant.

Other deep-diving research submarines are planned or under construction in the United States. These are in addition to those already in existence. They are in addition to the fleet of shallow-diving midget submarines that the United States has built up.

At the Portsmouth (New Hampshire) Naval Shipyard the Navy is building a diesel-battery-powered research submarine. She will be the U.S.S. *Dolphin,* AGS 555. Her keel was laid November 9, 1962, and her launch date probably will be around the end of 1967. The *Dolphin,* the office of the Assistant Secretary of Defense tells me, will be 152 feet long, will have an 18-foot beam, and when submerged will displace 930 tons. She will be used in oceanographic, acoustical, and antisubmarine warfare research.

After the *Thresher* sank, the Secretary of the Navy asked Rear Admiral Edward C. Stephan, the Navy's oceanographer and a veteran submariner, to serve as chairman of a new group to investigate locating, identifying, and recovering large, deeply submerged bodies on the ocean floor. This was named the Deep Submergence Systems Review Group. Serving along with Admiral Stephan were such figures as the retired skipper of U.S.S. *Nautilus,* William R. Anderson; Edwin A. Link, today of Ocean Systems, Inc., as is Admiral Stephan; and Dr. Allyn Vine of Woods Hole.

The work of the Deep Submergence Systems Review Group has led to plans for three Navy deep-diving submarines.

The first is a rescue submarine. She will be small (40 feet long, 8 feet in diameter, 25 tons in weight), with a 3-man crew, and may be transported by air to any place in the world within 24 hours. Upon arrival, she would be able to dive to a crippled submarine, fasten on to a hatch, and bring up 12 to 14 survivors a trip from the disabled craft. The rescued men would be transported to her mother ship, another submarine. She would discharge her survivors into the mother ship by means of attaching herself to a hatch underwater. In this manner, she could save men in a disabled nuclear submarine beneath the Arctic ice. But how she would hover over a sunken sub and attach herself to the hatch with a leakproof seal on the bottom of the sea under heavy pressure is a big question. To find out, say Samuel Feldman and Lincoln Cathers of the Deep Submergence Systems Project, the Navy is making many experiments and studying many methods.

A C-141 airplane would carry the rescue submarine to the scene of a sinking. The C-141, or *Star Lifter,* is America's and Lockheed's new cargo plane, huger than any plane before it. It became operational in April 1965. It is the only plane in existence that could carry the proposed rescue submarine. Another plane able to transport the submarine is on its way. This is the mammoth C-5A, being built by Lockheed for the U.S. Air Force, the biggest freight plane ever conceived. Its cargo compartment deck will be 19 feet wide by 13½ feet high by 145 feet long. It will be able to carry 1,000 passengers or 50 automobiles or any of the equipment of an entire U.S. Army infantry division: a helicopter, tank, missiles, trucks, and jeeps; or the rescue submarine.

The Navy expects to have its first rescue submarine ready in early 1969. Four more will be on station, it is hoped, by 1970.

The Navy hopes it never has to use a rescue submarine for a rescue. The only recent submarine disaster was that of the *Thresher,* and that tragedy occurred 24 years after the last previous submarine catastrophe. "It was recognized from the very beginning," says the Navy, "that a system designed only for personnel rescue would soon decay from disuse since the last disaster, the *Squalus,* was in 1939." So the Navy plans another use for its rescue craft: She, too, will help explore the sea.

The other two deep-diving craft the Navy is planning are: (1) a search submarine to search on the deep-sea floor; and (2) a recovery submarine to recover objects on the deep-sea floor. Both may eventually dive to 20,000 feet. They will have 3- or 4-man crews.

The 20,000-foot-deep craft will be 40 feet long and 10 feet in diameter. They will weigh 50,000 pounds, and will not themselves collapse short of a depth of 30,000 feet. They will have a speed of 5 knots that they can maintain for 4 hours, or 4 knots that they can maintain for 10 hours.

Both will be buoyant and will "fail safe"; they will have buoyancy inside their pressure hulls so that, if necessary, they will float to the surface on their own and bring up their crews with them. This was not always the case in deep-sea exploration. William Beebe's bathysphere, in which he reached a depth of 3,028 feet in 1934, was a one-piece, 5,000-pound steel casting, a heavy ball. It was not buoyant. If its line to the surface had snapped, the bathysphere would have plummeted to the bottom, taking its occupants to certain death.

The recovery submarine will have mechanical arms to pick up

small objects from the seabed; the search submarine will not need the arms.

Private companies also are building and planning new deep-diving and research submarines. Already built is Lear Siegler, Inc.'s, Benthos V, a submarine the owner hopes will help show how to take men off a wrecked submarine and thus contribute to the development of the Navy's rescue submarine. Benthos V dives only 600 feet, but there is no reason later models cannot go deeper.

North American Aviation, which has been building the Apollo capsules for the space ride to the moon, has designed the Beaver. The Beaver's specialty will be her arms and hands. North American has a Navy Bureau of Ships contract to develop the best possible mechanical arms and hands, or, as they are called, manipulators. The Beaver's hands already can wield wrenches, stud guns, jet pumps, wire brushes, grinding wheels, and cable cutters.

The Westinghouse Corporation, having just brought over the *Deepstar 4000* from France, working with Jacques-Yves Cousteau, plans three later Deepstars: for 2,000 feet; for 13,000 feet; and for 20,000 feet deep.

Grumman Aircraft & Engineering Co. and Giovanola, S.A., Switzerland, will build Jacques Piccard's PX-15, for a 2,000-foot depth.

International Hydrodynamics Co., Ltd., Vancouver, Canada, offers for lease the *Pisces,* for 5,000 feet.

General Motors Defense Research Laboratory is reported building a two-man, 6,000-foot-deep Geminaut.

Lockheed Missiles and Space Company is building the *Deep Quest*. This submarine will take a 7,000-pound payload over 1½ miles beneath the ocean's surface. Forty feet long, 16 feet in beam, weighing 50 tons, *Deep Quest* will be tear-shaped or whale-shaped. She will have a crew of two, and will be able to carry two observers in addition.

Divers will be able to leave *Deep Quest* on the shallow bottom and explore the floor around her. She will normally stay submerged 12 hours, with life support for the four men inside her for 48 hours.

Models of *Deep Quest* were tested at the Stevens Institute of Technology, Hoboken, New Jersey, and at the Southwest Research Institute, San Antonio, Texas. Her pressure hull is now being built at the Sun Ship Building & Dry Dock Company, Chester, Pennsylvania. Her sea trials were to begin in 1967.

Lockheed scientists and engineers also have proposed a revolutionary shaped exploring submarine, a flying saucer for liquid space. They call it a "vehicle designed to probe the deep, dark depths of the sea, and especially its bottom." It is called the *Turtle*. The *Turtle*'s extraordinary shape is that of a somewhat flattened turtle. The shape, Lockheed scientists believe, will make her very maneuverable just above the bottom.

The *Turtle* is the brainchild of P. E. Summers, a submarine veteran of World War II, and Dr. Willy Fiedler, who helped Lockheed develop and prove the Polaris missile.

When sediment hides an object on the ocean floor (such as ancient Spanish treasure), a hydrojet will be used by *Turtle* to scour away the sediment. Crablike arms will recover objects on the seabed. The *Turtle* could, Fiedler says, be a superior undersea garbage truck. Instead of just dumping radioactive waste, she could bury it in the sea floor and thus put it out of reach of currents that otherwise might spread it around.

For the pressure hulls of its 20,000-foot search and recovery submarines, the Navy is considering glass and fiber glass. Glass is a material that, preliminary tests have shown, is stronger than metals at the depth required. Glass actually is strengthened by the pressure of great depths.

"The 20,000-foot vehicle capsule," says Harold Bernstein, materials engineer for the Deep Submergence Systems Project, "will require extensive advances in material technology and a spectrum of materials will be considered ranging from high-strength steel to glass."

Already a small glass-ceramic-hulled submarine, 8 feet long and 1 foot in diameter, has been completed for the Navy, at Pennsylvania State University, by Jaroslav P. Stachiw, with help from the Corning Glass Works, Corning, New York. It was made to carry instruments, not men.

The model glass-ceramic submarine is believed capable of diving to the very bottom of the sea, seven miles down, like a bathyscaphe —far deeper than any other submarine. It will not, in all probability, make any such trip. The last I heard it was to be tested to destruction (to learn whatever that might take) in a dry-land pressure chamber.

Meanwhile, the Corning Glass people have drawn up plans for a 60-foot-long, 8-foot-diameter, man-carrying, deep-diving submarine. This one's entire bow will be of clear glass, like a goldfish bowl. It will have a hemispherical glass nose for viewing, not just a porthole to look through.

Furthermore, a glass bubble may carry 2 men 7 miles down to the bottoms of the deepest trenches—the first deep-diving device to reach as far down as the bathyscaphes. The bubble is expected to be tested soon. William B. McLean, the developer of the Sidewinder air-to-air missile, and technical director of the Naval Ordnance Test Station, China Lake, California, is developing it. It will let men see in any direction, and will let them stay at any depth for some time. Its glass, as it is compressed by the depths, will become stronger.

"Glass in compression is an extremely strong material and at the same time is comparatively light in weight," Willis R. Forman of the Naval Ordnance Test Station, China Lake, California, writes me. "These combined features of strength and light weight make it theoretically possible to construct underwater vehicles capable of going to the deepest parts of the ocean (36,000 feet). . . . It appears that a very small glass vehicle could operate at any ocean depth." A glass hull, Mr. Forman points out, will let pilots and scientists look around in any direction—omnidirectional viewing. Limited one-way visibility through a small port is today a handicap to men in deep-diving vehicles.

Strange as it seems, a man may be better protected 7 miles down by clear glass than he would be by a metal hull.

When Jules Verne wrote his famous book, the first successful submarine had just sunk her first ship. Horace L. Huntly of Mobile, Alabama, had built the 20-foot-long, 5-foot-deep, and 3½-foot-wide Confederate submarine *David*. Eight men turned a screw from inside the hull to propel *David*. Off Charleston, she placed a torpedo against, and sank, the Federal ironclad *Housatonic*. *David* also went down and took her crew with her. The modern submarine dates from the 1890's and 1900's, or more than 20 years after Verne's book. An American, John P. Holland, after working for years on the problem of how to build a submarine, sold his first, the *Holland,* to the U.S. Navy in 1900. That was the U.S. Navy's first submarine. The Navy ordered five more like her. The British also ordered five just like her. Meanwhile another American, Simon Lake, who was born in 1866, four years before Verne's novel appeared, was also at work. He designed the *Argonaut,* the first successful submarine to be used in salvaging sunken treasure. Lake was the first to use an internal combustion engine in a submarine, thus preparing the way for diesel engines. Germany completed two submarines in 1890, and began, in 1906, to take the submarine seriously as part of a construction program for her navy.

Almost 50 years later, on January 21, 1954, the United States launched the world's first nuclear submarine, the *Nautilus,* at Groton, Connecticut. But not till 1965 were submarines sufficiently developed so that the President could propose nuclear submarines that eventually would sail the abyss—almost four miles deep.

"The great depths of the ocean are entirely unknown to us," said Professor Arronax in Jules Verne's famous novel. As man enters the depths, that situation today is changing fast. "Who knows," asked Captain Nemo, "if in another hundred years we may not see a second *Nautilus?*" Our nuclear-powered exploring submarine, the new metal and glass submarines being built or planned by private industry, and the Navy's search and recovery and rescue submarines will be that—and much more besides.

America's exploring submarine, the White House said, "will enable scientists to examine firsthand an extensive part of the earth's surface for new sources of raw materials."

She could, the White House suggested, help speed the day of "deep depth mining."

The background behind that statement is that in the deep oceans, two or three miles down, there have been spotted what look like vast new supplies of minerals and raw materials.

Calcareous ooze, or globigerina ooze, which is composed mostly of minute calcareous skeletons of protozoa, covers about 48 percent, or 50 million square miles, of the deep ocean floor. In it there is calcium carbonate, used in cement rock. Siliceous ooze, from diatoms (microscopic plants) and radiolarians (microscopic animals), covers 14 million square miles of the Pacific floor. One type of siliceous ooze is diatomaceous earth. It could be used for anything for which diatomaceous earth which is found on land is now marketed: filtering agents, heat and sound insulators, concrete fillers, dusting agents, and so on.

Over wide areas the floor of the abyss appears dotted with mineral nodules. The nodules were first discovered in the 1870's by Britain's *Challenger,* then found around 1900 in the Pacific by Harvard's Alexander Agassiz. Deep-sea dredging, coring, and photographs on long Pacific ocean trips made in the 1950's by Scripps Institution ships showed that thousands of square miles of the Pacific bed were covered with the nodules, or chunks, of minerals. "What is probably the first ton of ore mined from the high seas," said *Naval Research Reviews* for April, 1963, "has been sent to the U.S. Metallurgy Research Center in Reno, Nevada, for study. The shipment consists of manganese nodules—roundish mineral lumps that resemble fire-blackened potatoes—dredged from a depth of 12,000 feet about 200 miles west-southwest of Cape San Lucas at the tip of Baja California, Mexico. The mining operation was carried out from the *Spencer F. Baird,* a research vessel of the Scripps Institution of Oceanography, which is supported by the Office of Naval Research."

John Mero, a research and engineering consultant, for years has studied the nodules. He feels they can be profitably mined. They are, he says, from one-half inch to 10 inches (or more) in diameter (a huge one recovered weighed 1,700 pounds). They are rich in manganese, nickel, cobalt, copper, or iron. The brown-to-earthy-black nodules also may provide molybdenum, vanadium, titanium. Manganese, which today we get mainly from Africa, is essential in the making of steel. Metalworking is the United States' biggest and most important industrial activity. Manganese is therefore essential to our standard of living.

"One manganese 'ore province,' " C. P. Idyll reports in *Abyss,* "off the coasts of North and South America in the Pacific Ocean, covers two million square miles and contains a conservatively estimated 26 billion tons of ore! This quantity is based on the assumption the nodules average only one pound per square foot, whereas five to seven pounds per square foot may be a closer estimate." In the Pacific the nodules are believed to be everywhere except in the deep trenches, and they actually reach to about 23,000 feet down in the Marianas Trench. In the Atlantic the nodules are richer in iron, and are found off the east coast on the Blake Plateau and the Muir Seamount. Some seamounts in both the Atlantic and the Pacific are coated with manganese crusts.

How the nodules have been formed, apparently over millions of years, is one of the mysteries of the sea. One belief is that some were built by small animals, microscopic creatures that set up housekeeping on such objects as sharks' teeth, whales' earbones, particles of clay, or other small objects on the bottom of the sea.

(Some but not all of the nodules have such nuclei.) These tiny animals consume seawater, the theory goes, and from it extract the minerals they deposit and so build up the nodules. Dr. John W. Graham of Woods Hole explains:

> The metal balls were produced by living organisms. They contained the tiny shell of a foraminifer, a one-cell organism, right in the center. When this died an even smaller organism, as yet unidentified, settled on the outer wall of the foraminifer shell, attracted by the latter's protein content. The new organism . . . used sea water for food. It derived valuable metals from it and concentrated them in and around itself. It was a natural mine! That is why the nodules are so full of mineral substances.

The unidentified microscopic animals are so efficient at extracting minerals from the water that the nodules on the deep-sea floor seem to be constantly increasing in number. There are enough sharks' teeth to help ensure this occurrence. Sharks grow enough of them; they never stop growing teeth, and a single tooth may be replaced a hundred times in a shark's lifetime. (This perpetual replacement of teeth is common to sharks and crocodiles.) Sharks' teeth, therefore, are about as plentiful an item as you can find on the seabed. You can buy them as souvenirs in many a beach resort. They are also found on land. Ancient sharks' teeth have been discovered in Indiana, Alabama, Maryland, New York, South Carolina, New Jersey, New Mexico, Idaho, Wyoming, Kansas, and from Sharktooth Hill, near Bakersfield, California. On land or beneath the sea, sharks' teeth are hard, and do not deteriorate. They—and those whales' earbones—are about the only objects, William Beebe explained, that are not dissolved by the deep sea.

Some fossil sharks' teeth from Sharktooth Hill have been 6 inches long. The prehistoric shark from which they came would have been almost 100 feet long. The biggest fish ever known, this monster was named *Carcharodon*. Based on these teeth, the American Museum of Natural History made a model of *Carcharodon*'s jaws. The jaws are big enough for a man to stand in with his arms outspread.

Carcharodon furnishes a giant-size mystery: some of its teeth, 4 inches long, were dredged up in the Pacific in this century. They appeared fresh—not fossil—teeth. The fact that they were dredged up, not buried by silt, also indicated that they had only recently been dropped. How could this be? Is *Carcharodon* still alive?

The nodules could be located by men aboard submarines like the *Aluminaut* or future exploring submarines either visually or with magnetometers (which locate metal), after which they could be sucked up by three-mile-long vacuum hoses. The hoses might be somewhat like those used by the *Essayons,* the world's biggest sea-going dredge, which is operated by the Army's Corps of Engineers. *Essayons* normally keeps open ship channels in and around New York Harbor, but she helped clear out the Suez Canal a few years ago.

The vacuum hoses might deposit their nodules in an undersea mining camp located on the continental shelf, where men might live underwater as they did in Sealabs I and II (Chapter 18). Three companies already are working on undersea mining: the International Minerals and Chemical Corporation of Skokie, Illinois, a company in mining and processing minerals used in fertilizers; the Lockheed Missiles and Space Company, an aviation, space, and oceanographic firm; and Merritt-Chapman and Scott, an engineering construction firm. Two ships from the Department of the Interior's Oceanographic Center at Tiburon, California, are already conducting mining investigations. Professor A. M. Gaudin of the Massachusetts Institute of Technology sees vacuuming up the nodules as a development to be expected. "Just as open-pit mining has revolutionized the mining industry in my lifetime," he says, "so undersea mining may do it for our children."

Whether or not the whales' earbones and the sharks' teeth can be mined economically remains to be seen—but there may be trillions of dollars of wealth in the nodules on the sea floor.

The sea floor may even show us where to look for new supplies of fresh water on land. The 1965 Joint Oceanographic Institution's Deep Earth Sampling program (JOIDES) found fresh water 22 miles off northern Florida, on the Blake Plateau, a plain beneath 3,500 feet of water. The bed of water may reach beneath the land; locating it beneath the sea may show men where to sink their wells on land.

JOIDES also found evidence of phosphate (for fertilizer) by drilling beneath the continental shelf's sea floor off Georgia and northern Florida. The JOIDES expedition was conducted by four of the United States' and the world's largest oceanographic institutions: Columbia University's Lamont Geological Observatory; Woods Hole; the Institute of Marine Sciences at the University of Miami; and Scripps. The JOIDES results, Columbia's Maurice Ewing said, showed the necessity for drilling into the sea floor if you want to be certain what's there.

The motor vessel *Caldrill* did the drilling, six holes in all, for JOIDES. Hole No. 2 went 1,050 feet into the floor of the Atlantic —the deepest penetration of the ocean bottom for scientific purposes on record. Hole No. 3 was drilled 250 miles offshore in 3,386 feet of water, the greatest water depth anyone in the Atlantic ever has drilled through.

In all history up to date, the most useful single substance that man so far has discovered is said by some to be petroleum. (Man did not have to discover water or air; they were vital to his existence.) Petroleum goes into thousands of products from plastics to synthetic fibers to telephones; as a fuel, it warms your home; as a source of energy, it turns factory wheels and runs all forms of mechanical transportation except those driven by nuclear power or coal; as a lubricant, it is essential for the moving parts of all machines—it is the only lubricant that can satisfactorily oil the cars, trains, planes, and ships that carry you wherever you go and the machines that manufacture the goods you use.

But if petroleum has been the most useful substance in the recent past, there is a possibility that seawater, one of the commonest things on the globe and which engulfs seven-tenths of our planet, can become the most useful substance of the future. Seawater itself may be of more value to man even than the minerals on the bottom of the oceans. The water contains billions of tons of dissolved minerals. How can we learn to extract the things we can use from it? Those animals we cannot see, living on whales' earbones or sharks' teeth on the bottom of the oceans, may be able to provide information that will assist mankind beyond measure in the generations ahead.

We do not know how the microscopic creatures do it. If we could learn from them, it would help immeasurably. We have learned how to extract magnesium from the sea. This is done at Freeport, Texas, by the Dow Chemical Company. It came about because during World War II we desperately needed magnesium alloys for airplane construction. Seawater contains 5¾ million tons of magnesium per cubic mile. Getting it out meant lighter and stronger alloys for aircraft, which helped make possible our tremendous production of warplanes during World War II. Magnesium also went into incendiary bombs, star shells, and tracer bullets. Today it goes into medicines, toothpaste, printing ink, and spaceships.

The Dow company also obtains from seawater about 80 percent of the bromine the nation uses for ethyl gasoline and medicines. Magnesium, bromine, and salt, which man has obtained for centuries by evaporating seawater, are about all we get at present in quantity out of the water itself.

This is but a fraction of the minerals in the ocean. Most elements are present in seawater, some only in infinitesimal amounts. A single cubic mile of seawater, the American Machine and Foundry Company points out, contains 165 million tons of minerals, and there are 330 million cubic miles of seawater in the oceans! The minerals include gypsum, potash, gold (but only a penny's worth to a million gallons of seawater), silver (there is far more silver in the sea than man has ever mined from the land). American Machine and Foundry's present efforts to do something about all this take the form of producing a slurry from the seawater that is sold to industry and agriculture.

There is drawing nearer every day, it appears, the time when many of us will drink the sea. Some people already do. A single cubic mile of seawater could supply New York City with all its water needs for four years—and New York City, like much of the rest of the United States, has been having periodic droughts. Just as you would expect, there is more water than anything else in the sea (salt is the next most common constituent). How to get the salt and water apart is easy. It can be done by half a dozen methods. How to do it cheaply enough is not so easy. But speeding the day when this will be a reality are the Office of Saline Water of the Department of the Interior and many private companies. Westinghouse has built in Kuwait, in the Middle East, a single plant that desalts 5,230,000 gallons of sea a day. General Electric Company, the Bogue Electric Company, the Struthers Wells Corporation of Warren, Pennsylvania, Scientific Design Company of New York City, Ionics, Inc., and Aqua-Chem, Inc., are in the field of desalinization. Fred A. Loebel, president of Aqua-Chem, Inc., of Waukesha, Wisconsin, which has erected 4,000 desalting installations that produce 18 million gallons of water a day over the world, says the cost of desalting already can be low. He figures 25 to 30 cents a thousand gallons—in a nuclear plant that would produce 150 million gallons daily. He advocates such a plant for New York City, and predicts a total world desalination capacity of a billion gallons daily by 1972—much of it in the United States. Since 1950, he says, the world desalting capacity has about doubled every three years. Our naval base at Guantánamo Bay, Cuba, gets its water by desalting the sea. One of a number of towns that drink desalted water is Freeport, Texas, near Houston, where a single plant supplies all the town's requirements. "Come down and have a drink of our supercharged, pure seawater," writes Elbert Turner of the Houston *Post*.

Fresh water is an absolute necessity not only to grow crops and to sustain life but for industry as well. It takes thousands of gallons to make a ton of steel or aluminum; it takes 200,000 gallons to make a ton of explosives for defense or for excavation; it takes 240,000 gallons of ultra-pure water to produce one ton of acetate for rayon and plastics, and 600,000 gallons for a ton of synthetic rubber.

Desalting seawater may be of most use to coastal towns like Freeport, but it will also be of much service inland. Much of the earth's land area has beneath it salty or brackish water that could be made fresh by the same methods.

From a shark's tooth on the midocean floor to the very water itself, rolling onto a beach, the sea holds unlimited possibilities for man.

The Middle Depths
Yield a Queer Fish

ONE HOT SUMMER NIGHT in 1964, at sea near the northern Bahamas, a small knot of fishermen hauled in a fish the like of which not one among them had caught before.

That the fishermen, ten altogether, were stumped by a queer fish, was surprising. For they were among the world's most knowledgeable fishermen. Between them they could recognize almost any known fish there is. They were ocean scientists and graduate students of oceanography and life in the sea from the Institute of Marine Science at the University of Miami, and their guests. They were aboard their new R/V (Research Vessel) *John Elliott Pillsbury,* a converted Navy ship. The puzzled, head-scratching fishermen included Chief Scientist Dr. Donald P. de Sylva, Dr. Anthony J. Provenzano, Jorge Cabrera of Mexico City, Dr. Brian Hazlett, Martin Roessler, Richard Daly, Wesley Lins, Jon Staiger, William Eschmeyer, and William M. Stephens.

Their catch was, it turned out, a fish no man on earth ever had seen before. It was a fish too weird, in fact, for any fisherman or anyone else even to have dreamed about: a small, solid-black, squatty creature with big, comic-strip bug eyes. The men goggled right back. The fish, a tiny thing one inch long, actually dragged a trawl—or something like a trawl—behind it. A long stringlike filament, attached to a ventral (lower) fin, streamed out behind. At the end of the filament there were a number of leafy appendages, each one displaying an orange luminescent spot. These appendages apparently sweep through the water behind the fish like a trawl being towed behind a fishing boat. No such method of capturing prey, if that is what it is, had been known before.

The fish had come out of one of the most mysterious parts of the oceans: the weed-filled area of the North Atlantic known as the Sargasso Sea, where few ships travel. It presumably came from the midwater depths from 1,000 to 6,000 feet (over a mile) beneath the surface—the very depths that the new U.S. deep-diving submarine, the *Alvin,* will search. Here, more or less, halfway between the surface and the sea floor of the open ocean, is an almost unknown region men are struggling to learn something about. These middle depths have been too deep for most floating nets or baited lines. Trawls have been easier to use on the bottom of the sea. The little mystery fish was caught in a plankton net.

The more the new fish was studied, the stranger it became. After the *Pillsbury* returned to Miami, Dr. C. R. Robins, Curator of Fishes at the Institute of Marine Science, examined it. It was not only a new species, he said; it was a new genus, and, in fact, an entirely new family of fishes.

Wrote William M. Stephens, who was along on the Sargasso Sea trip:

> The discovery of the new fish (which Dr. Robins and Chief Scientist de Sylva have named *Kasidoron edom*) illustrates an interesting truth: the oceans are still largely untapped. Eons of time are required for a distinct family of fishes to evolve. In the great expanses of the black depths there must be a sizable population of *Kasidoron* swimming about. Otherwise, how could enough of them find mates to perpetuate their kind? Yet the first representative of the group was seen by man in 1964. . . .
>
> How many other strange fishes unknown to science are swimming about in the never-never regions of the sea?

The principal purpose of the Miami expedition was to locate the centers of the spawning activity of the white marlin and blue marlin. A high-speed plankton sampler helped. This sampler, a new development by the U.S. Fish and Wildlife Service, is a sort of bucket that can be towed fairly fast (at 8 knots) and thus catches fairly fast fish. On its first tow it caught a larval (young) marlin. During the cruise it trapped hundreds of tiny larval fishes: marlins, tunas, barracudas, wahoo, dolphin, swordfish, ocean sunfish, others. It shed some light, therefore, on where all of these fish are born and start growing up.

For once it was the smallest (and youngest) fish, not the biggest ones, that the Miami fishermen hoped would not get away. They didn't. The expedition caught a perfectly formed baby sailfish, with sail, bill, and all, 1½ inches long. (Six months after leaving the egg, a sailfish is 5 feet long.) The youngster was taken by a midwater trawl from the same depths where the *Kasidoron edom* came from.

"Placed in a shallow pan," said Stephens, "it continuously circled the container, its fragile sail held proudly erect."

In a trawl 2,000 feet down, 100 miles off Fernandina Beach, Florida, the expedition caught a completely grown deep-water shark, *Galeus*—only 12 inches long. A male, it was placed in a shipboard aquarium, where it seemed to adjust. But when the time came for movies to be made of it and the floodlights were turned on, the little shark was shocked, seemed paralyzed, and at once died. "Accustomed to living in total darkness," says Stephens, "it was evidently killed by the bright lights." A deep-sea squid also died under the floodlights. Other animals, some from far deeper, seemed not in the slightest affected by bright lights. Why some are stricken, and some not, is a mystery of the sea.

A big one did get away from the Institute of Marine Science expedition: a large, unidentified animal swam into a net and carried it away.

In aquariums aboard the *Pillsbury* there were made for the first time movies of some subjects no man ever had filmed before, such as a rare pelagic octopus (the dwarf paper nautilus) giving birth; a rainbow-hued flying fish as small as an artificial fly used in trout fishing; and pteropods—winged snails that flutter through the water like moths.

The party also photographed the larvae of eels, crabs, and lobsters, baby octopuses, and f021fuck copepods of many colors.

The men at night hung waterproof lights over the side of the *Pillsbury,* just beneath the surface of the sea, and scooped up in dip nets the animals they attracted. Night-lighting brought in flying fishes, squirrelfish, squids, puffers, jacks, and filefishes. Two young silver-blue squirrelfish in only two days changed to the red of the adult squirrelfish of the coral reefs, right in a shipboard aquarium.

"In the southern part of the Sargasso Sea," Stephens reported, "we made our deepest trawls with the Isaacs-Kidd." This is a recent invention, a middle-depth trawl used between surface and sea floor. The men let out 16,400 feet of wire. They got, among other deep-sea fishes, two rare gulper eels, strange flabby fishes that are mostly mouth and are capable of swallowing prey larger than themselves. They also took the smaller snipe eel and the extraordinary *Ipnops,* which has no eyes but possesses light-sensitive plates where eyes ordinarily would be. "In our deep plankton tows," Stephens said, "we took many larval deep-sea fishes as well as the young of surface fishes. We were surprised at the richness of the plankton, as the Sargasso Sea is traditionally considered a fairly sterile area."

Off the Bahamas, the men caught in the plankton sampler the larva of a marlin less than one-eighth of an inch long, the smallest Atlantic marlin ever caught. The biggest blue marlin ever caught on rod and reel (by John Battles at St. Thomas, Virgin Islands, on July 26, 1964) measured 13 feet 8 inches in length, 5 feet 9 inches in girth, and was 814 pounds in weight. The biggest white marlin ever reeled in (by L. F. Hooper off Miami Beach on March 20,

1938) measured 8 feet 8 inches in length, 2 feet 9 inches in girth, and weighed 161 pounds.

A black marlin was, in fact, the largest gamefish ever taken on a rod and reel. It was caught off Cabo Blanco, Peru, by Alfred C. Glassell, Jr., of Houston, Texas, on August 4, 1953. You can see it (an estimated 2½ million persons each year do) in the Hall of Life in the Sea on the first floor of the Museum of Natural History at the Smithsonian Institution, Washington, D.C. It weighed 1,560 pounds and measured 14 feet 6 inches in length and 6 feet 9 inches in girth. It took Mr. Glassell 1 hour 45 minutes to bring the marlin alongside his boat. The marlin meanwhile made 49 jumps clear of the water. Movies made as Mr. Glassell caught the black marlin were dubbed into the film *The Old Man and the Sea.*

Two world's record sharks caught on rod and reel were bigger than Mr. Glassell's black marlin and are the only rod-and-reel catches listed by the International Gamefish Association that were bigger. A 2,664-pound white shark, a man-eater, was caught by Alfred Dean off Ceduna, South Australia, on April 21, 1959. It was 16 feet 10 inches long and 9 feet 6 inches around. A 1,780-pound tiger shark was caught by Walter Maxwell near Cherry Grove, South Carolina, on June 14, 1964. It was 13 feet 10½ inches long and 8 feet 7 inches in girth.

Based on the catches of marlin larvae, Miami's Chief Scientist de Sylva believes there are three major marlin spawning grounds in the western Atlantic: northeast of Little Bahama Bank, near Abaco; northwest of Grand Bahama Island; and southwest of Bermuda. Thus was the expedition's main objective—to locate the spawning grounds of the marlin—achieved.

The men also caught many bristlemouths, or *Cyclothones*. This fish, one of the stomiatoids not sought by fishermen and rarely even thought of by men ashore, nevertheless is probably the most common of all fishes in the sea. Throughout the world *Cyclothones* inhabit the middepths in almost unbelievable numbers. Like most midwater fishes, they are rarely more than a few inches long.

The *Cyclothones* are known as bristlemouths because their mouths actually bristle with teeth. Their mouths open wide till the jaws are nearly in a straight line when a meal seems to be approaching.

Most stomiatoids are small—*Aristostomias grimaldii* is about 5½ inches long. Although William Beebe once saw a 6-foot-long stomiatoid from his bathysphere window, no such big one ever has been caught.

One stomiatoid, *Idiacanthus panamensis*, C. P. Idyll reports, swims perhaps a mile deep by day, then comes almost to the surface by night—a remarkable vertical journey, and one of the longest up-and-down trips known to be made by ocean creatures.

But unquestionably the most spectacular catch of the entire Sargasso Sea cruise was *Kasidoron edom,* the unknown fish from a new family that nobody can explain. It swam about in an aquarium aboard ship, but could not adjust to the aquarium. "For this was a fish from the dark midwaters," said Stephens, "where there are no solid barriers. It had never before known containment. Now surrounded by barriers, it continually bumped into the sides of the aquarium and struggled in the sand on the bottom—trying, perhaps, to return to the pressures of the depths, away from the glaring lights."

Continued Stephens, "From the standpoint of science, the discovery of a new family of highly unusual fishes must be given top rank in importance. According to Dr. C. R. Robins, the expedition would have been a success if we had done nothing during the entire three-week cruise but catch that tiny black fish with the weird dangling appendages."

CHAPTER
13

A Half Mile Down,

They Led the Way

WILLIAM BEEBE and Otis Barton peered into the depths from which no man had ever returned alive. In a ball-shaped bathysphere, swinging at the end of a long line from the surface, they were 2,900 feet beneath the sea. At the time, only dead men had sunk below 600 feet. Beebe and Barton each had a 6-inch porthole with a transparent quartz pane through which they could gaze out into the darkness of the deep sea. Through one of the portholes the beams of a searchlight moderated the darkness.

A strange fish swam into view: "It was less than 3 feet long, rather slender, with many small luminous spots on the body, and a relatively large, pale-green, crescent-shaped light under the eye," Beebe recalled.

No one ever has identified what that one was.

"Near it," said Beebe, "were five lantern fish. They swam so slowly that I made certain before they disappeared that they were of the genus *Lampadena.*"

The men were over a half mile below the surface of the sea— the record depth at the time, August 11, 1934, for human penetration beneath the ocean.

Beebe wrote in *Half Mile Down,*

> At 11:12 A.M., we came to rest gently at 3,000 feet, and I knew that this was my ultimate floor; the cable on the winch was very near its end. A few days ago the

water had appeared blacker at 2,500 feet than could be imagined, yet now to this same imagination it seemed to show as blacker than black. It seemed as if all future nights in the upper world must be considered only relative degrees of twilight. I could never again use the word *black* with any conviction.

They reached their farthest point down, 3,028 feet, at a point 6 miles off Bermuda in water 1 mile deep. Their descent in the bathysphere was, so far as a single event can be pinpointed, the first major step in man's efforts to put eyewitnesses down into the depths of the sea.

Beebe and Barton showed the way then, over thirty years ago, to all of the men who are exploring the ocean's secrets today.

William Beebe became one of the first two eyewitnesses of the abyss because always, as a boy and as a man, his whole life had been devoted to observing things. He wanted to see for himself. Beebe said of the bathysphere dives, "The hope of . . . observations was the sole object of the entire project."

After graduating from Columbia, Beebe had been curator of ornithology at the New York Zoological Society, the world-famous Bronx Zoo. Birdwatching around the world was not enough for Beebe; he brought great water birds back so the public could watch them. In a mammoth (55 feet high, 75 feet wide, 152 feet long) flying-cage made of steel-pipe arches and netting, he placed on public view American and European flamingos, scarlet ibis, great blue herons, great white herons, little blue herons, snowy egrets, and white pelicans.

"The large flying-cage at the Zoo was installed with some apprehension," Dr. Beebe's wife, Mrs. Elswyth Thane Beebe, said, "as it was the first time a number of different species of birds had been required to live together in captivity, and there was some question as to whether they would keep the peace. He insisted that they would, and the flying-cage has been a feature of zoos ever since. I think Regent's Park in London adopted it soon after."

Beebe became interested in insects and went to British Guiana to see for himself. He watched the leaf-cutting ants at work—each ant carries a leaf high over its back, like a parasol. He became interested in mammals and studied the vampire bat: "They entered the bungalow at night and flew about . . . eventually one would settle down on an exposed foot or arm. . . ." Then the vampire bat draws out the blood, said Beebe, with only a small bite that would not awaken a sleeper.

After birds, insects, and bats, Beebe turned to observing life in the sea, and dived down to explore the shallow waters of tropical bays and harbors before he explored far deeper in the bathysphere.

Otis Barton had well earned his position as the other of the first two eyewitnesses of the depths. He had provided time, thought, and money to bring the bathysphere into existence. Designed by Captain John H. J. Butler, it was a blue ball of thick steel, 1¼ inches thick, with only the tiny quartz windows to gaze out of. It weighed 5,400 pounds. Rudders kept it in place (kept it, that is, facing one way, more or less). Oxygen tanks fitted to the inside walls provided the divers' air supply. A chemical powder helped to absorb the carbon dioxide the men exhaled. A small (14 inches in diameter) manhole permitted only slim men to enter. For a dive the manhole was sealed with a 400-pound lid. There were no seats. The bathysphere was 4 feet 9 inches in diameter, so there was no room to stand up. The two men squatted on the steel floor. It was hot; Beebe fanned himself with a palm-leaf fan during descents in the bathysphere. He always carried along a copy of Murray and Hjort's *The Depths of the Ocean.*

A single phone line reached the surface. The people on the ship overhead were so concerned with the safety of Beebe and Barton that only five seconds were allowed to elapse if the men in the bathysphere remained silent. They had to chatter continually to the surface—to Gloria Hollister, who took down what they said, and to John Tee-Van of the Bronx Zoo, among others. On September 22, 1932, Beebe made a radio broadcast over the network of the National Broadcasting Company from the end of the phone line, 1,500 to 2,200 feet deep. He talked with Miss Hollister on the deck of the surface ship. This was the first time radio engineers had traveled beyond territorial waters of the United States to broadcast a program back to their stations.

How dangerous the bathysphere was is shown by one incident. Once when lowered empty in a test, it sprang a leak and, at a great depth, filled with water under great pressure. After the bathysphere was back on deck of the mother ship, Beebe wrenched off the 14-inch-diameter door, and a jet of water under terrific pressure (as if from a fire hydrant) shot across the deck. Beebe wrote that it could have knocked a man's head off.

Before the half-mile dive, the bathysphere had been on display at the 1933 Century of Progress Exhibition in Chicago. "During this time half a million people thrust their heads within the narrow doorway," said Beebe, "and murmured, 'Thank Heaven, we don't have to go under water in this.' "

Beebe encountered an unknown monster on his half-mile dive:

At 2,450 feet a very large, dim, but not indistinct outline came into view for a fraction of a second, and at 2,500 a delicately illumined ctenophore jelly throbbed past. Without warning, the large fish returned and this time I saw its complete, shadowlike contour as it passed through the farthest end of the beam. Twenty feet is the least possible estimate I can give to its full length, and it was deep in proportion. The whole fish was monochrome, and I could not see even an eye or a fin. For the majority of the "size-conscious" human race this MARINE MONSTER would, I suppose, be the supreme sight of the expedition. In shape it was a deep oval, it swam without evident effort, and it did not return. . . .

What this great creature was I cannot say. A first, and most reasonable guess would be a small whale or blackfish. We know that whales have a special chemical adjustment of the blood which makes it possible for them to dive a mile or more, and come up without getting the "bends." So this paltry depth of 2,450 feet would be nothing for any similarly equipped cetacean. Or, less likely, it may have been a whale shark, which is known to reach a length of 40 feet. Whatever it was it appeared and vanished so unexpectedly and showed so dimly that it was quite unidentifiable except as a large living creature.

The whale shark Beebe mentioned may have been over 40 feet long—they might be as much as 50 or 60 feet. Aside from the biggest whales, they are the hugest creatures in the sea. A 38-foot whale shark caught at Knight's Key, Florida, weighed 26,594 pounds.

Because whales are really mammals, the whale shark is the biggest fish in the sea—it is the longest and the heaviest. It feeds on small sea life. The first one any man ever saw was a 15-foot-long whale shark in Table Bay, Cape of Good Hope, less than 150 years ago. Since then this white-spotted animal has been observed about once a year on the average by men.

Beebe himself observed whale sharks off Cape San Lucas, Mexico. He looked down into the Pacific from its surface and "the effect was of the water being suddenly filled with a vast number of unconnected drifting spots of white." With John Tee-Van and Jocelyn Crane in a small boat, he followed a whale shark. "We watched shark suckers, some more than two feet in length, slither over his great body," Beebe said. The whale shark's head was blunt and broad. Beebe looked down the giant throat. "The mouth," he said, "was fully six feet across. The teeth in the huge maw were arranged in great sheets, consisting of thousands upon thousands of denticles each about an eighth of an inch in length." The whale shark could not have swallowed Jonah, however; the throat is only four inches in diameter. The whale shark cannot, Captain Bill Gray of the Miami Seaquarium says, swallow an object even as big as a grapefruit.

"The tail fin was enormous and swept regularly back and forth like some part of a mighty engine," Beebe continued, "its tip swinging from one side to the other in three seconds through a space of ten feet." The whale shark, huge though it is, is gentle and inoffensive and even when harpooned never has been known to attack a man or a boat. It can make men worry, however. Tuna fishermen fear that the whale shark can knock a rudder or propeller off a fishing boat with a flick of its tail. And it can get tangled in and destroy fishing nets. Ships sometimes run into whale sharks, with stories of sea serpents likely to result from such incidents.

Although Beebe and Barton descended in the bathysphere far deeper than anyone before them, they were by no means the first divers to go down inside a shell containing air. The first to do so in all history, presumably, was the water spider. The water spider weaves its silken sheet *beneath* the surfaces of ponds. From the surface the spider brings down bubbles of air that it places inside the sheet. In this air-filled underwater home the water spider lives, courts, and protects its eggs—and it probably has been doing so for millions of years.

The first man to go down inside something like a diving bell for a peep beneath the sea may have been Alexander the Great, king of Macedon and conqueror of Persia in the fourth century B.C. A thirteenth-century manuscript shows the young man, who sought new worlds to conquer and who was tutored by Aristotle, inside a barrel-shaped, apparently glass-sided underwater compartment. He appears to be only a few feet down. He is said to have seen (as did Beebe) a monster beneath the sea. Alexander's monster took three days to swim past his glass barrel, one tale of ancient days relates, and that tale has been told in books and articles about the sea serpent ever since.

In all probability the first American to go down beneath the sea in an air-filled compartment was Sergeant Ezra Lee who, during the American Revolution, made a trip in the *Turtle*, an undersea craft designed by David Bushnell. Bushnell, a Yale university student, had tried to invent a device to combat big wooden British battleships. His *Turtle,* the first so-called submarine (but not the type that led to today's submarines), was built of wood and carried one man. The man cranked one screw to propel the *Turtle,* and

cranked another screw to make it climb. Ezra Lee sailed it to
Lord Howe's flagship one summer night, carrying an explosive
charge to be screwed onto the flagship's wooden bottom. But the
bottom was sheathed in copper, the scheme would not work, and
Sergeant Lee had to give up his attack. He cranked Bushnell's
one-man submarine away from the flagship.

The next man and next American to go down inside an air-
filled chamber was Robert Fulton, who in 1801 descended to a
depth of 25 feet in a submarine he had constructed and stayed
down four hours.

No American or anyone else had got very deep until Beebe and
Barton came along. Before making their record half-mile dive
they had made others in the bathysphere, setting deeper and deeper
marks each time. One dive was 250 feet down, one 410, one 803,
one 1,428 feet, one 2,200, one 2,510. As the first eyewitnesses of
the depths, Beebe and Barton opened up the world far beneath the
sea to the eyes of men. Many of the animals they saw were unknown and puzzling to them. Said William Beebe after his dives:
"I have 154 separate and distinct notes on unknown fish, and 225
notes on unknown animals." Here are some of the sights Beebe
saw on various dives:

> *500 feet:* Here for the first time I saw strange, ghostly,
> dark forms hovering in the distance—forms which never
> came nearer, but reappeared at deeper, darker depths.
> Flying snails passed in companies of 50 or more, looking
> like brown bubbles. I had seen them alive in the net
> hauls, but here they were at home in thousands.

> *600 feet:* Again a great cloud of a body moved in the
> distance—this time pale, much lighter than the water.
> How I longed for a single near view, or telescopic eyes
> which could pierce the murk. I felt as if some astonish-
> ing discovery lay just beyond the power of my eyes.

> *700 feet:* At another hundred feet a dozen fish passed
> the sphere swimming almost straight upright ... I had
> a flash only of the biggest fish yet—dark, with long,

tapering tail and quite a foot in length. Shrimps and snails drifted past like flakes of unheard-of storms. Also a large transparent jellyfish bumped against the glass, its stomach filled with a glowing mass of luminous food.

900 feet: A mist of crustaceans and flapping snails. . . . We both agreed that the light was quite bright enough to read by and then we tried Pica type and found that our eyes showed nothing definite whatever.

1,000 feet: We had a moment's excitement when a loop of black, sea-serpenty hose swung around before us, a jet-black line against blackish blue.

1,400 feet (a quarter of a mile down): I peered down and again I felt the old longing to go farther, although it looked like the black pitmouth of hell itself—yet still showed blue. I thought I saw a new fish flapping close to the sphere, but it proved to be the waving edge of the Explorers' club flag—black as jet at this depth.

1,750 feet: Six fish, each with a double line of lights down the side of the body.

1,850 feet: A single large fish, which we estimated to be four feet in length, went by . . . so rapidly that I got only a fleeting glimpse of many lights along a rather deep body. Once a school of large squids balanced near me. . . . Their great eyes, each illumined with a circle of colored lights, stared in at me—those unbelievable intelligent yet reasonless eyes backed by no brain and set in a snail.

1,950 feet: We got our first bad pitching. It was unexpected and I cut my lip and forehead against the window ledge and Barton struck his head against the door.

2,200 feet: I would focus on some one creature and just as its outlines began to be distinct on my retina, some brilliant, animated comet or constellation would rush across the small arc of my submarine heaven and every sense would be distracted, and my eyes would involuntarily shift to this new wonder. . . . While we hung in mid-ocean . . . a fish poised just to the left of my window, its elongate outline distinct and its dark sides lighted from sources quite concealed from me. It was an effective example of indirect lighting, with the glare of the photophores turned inward. I saw it very clearly and knew it as something wholly different from any deep-sea fish which had yet been captured by man. It turned slowly head-on toward me, and every ray of illumination vanished, together with its outline and itself—it simply was not, yet I knew it had not swum away.

2,100 feet: I had the most exciting experience of the whole dive. Two fish went very slowly by, not more than 6 or 8 feet away, each of which was at least 5 feet in length. They were of the general shape of large barracudas, but with shorter jaws which were kept wide open all the time I watched them. A single line of strong lights, pale bluish, was strung down the body. The usual second line was quite absent. The eyes were very large, even for the great length of the fish. The undershot jaw was armed with numerous fangs which were illumined either by mucus or indirect internal lights. . . . This is the fish I subsequently named *Bathysphaera intacta*, the Untouchable Bathysphere fish.

1,900 feet: I saw by the light of our electric beam . . . one of the true giant female anglerfish, a full 2 feet in length, with enormous mouth and teeth, deep and thick, with a long tentacle arising from the top of its head.

550 feet: Big leptocephalus undulated past, a pale ribbon of transparent gelatin with only the two iridescent eyes to indicate its arrival. As it moved I could see the outline faintly—10 inches long at least, and as it passed close, even the parted jaws were visible. This was the larva of some great sea eel.

980–2,000 feet: Class *Ascidiacea*; order *Ascidiae luciae.* Pyrosoma colonies up to one foot in length were observed a half dozen times. All except one of these was completely aglow with tiny pinpoints of light. These organisms are rare in the trawling nets, as usually one small colony, several inches in length, is caught for every 20 nets drawn. Occasionally, during certain months, the nets are almost filled with long, rope-like colonies several feet in length. [Pyrosoma colonies may be the sea-serpentlike organisms Jon Lindbergh sees on his dives.]

Beebe's firsthand observations deep in the ocean led him to believe that living creatures were far more abundant in the depths than had been thought. "I never anticipated it," he said, "and I have no adequate theory to account for it. The fact remains that a much more abundant and larger-sized fish fauna exists in these waters than is in any way adumbrated by six years of trawling with the best possible oceanographic outfit."

Here is another result that Beebe himself felt:

As fish after fish swam into my restricted line of vision —fish, which, heretofore, I had seen only dead and in my nets—as I saw their colors and their absence of colors, their activities and modes of swimming and clear evidence of their sociability or solitary habits, I felt that all the trouble and cost and risk were repaid many fold. For two years I had been studying the deep-sea fish in a limited area of mid-ocean . . . and now when we were at the bottom of our pendulum I realized that I, myself, was down where many hundreds of nets had been hauled. During the coming year I should be able to appreciate the plankton and fish hauls as never before. After these dives were past, when I can again examine the deep-sea treasures in my nets, I would feel as an astronomer might who looks through his telescope after having rocketed to Mars and back, or like a paleontologist who could suddenly annihilate time and see his fossils alive.

Beebe thought that outer space must be like the depths of the ocean:

> The only other place comparable to these marvelous nether regions must surely be naked space itself, out far beyond atmosphere, between the stars, where sunlight has no grip upon the dust and rubbish of planetary air, where the blackness of space, the shining planets, comets, suns, and stars must really be closely akin to the world of life as it appears to the eyes of an awed human being, in the open ocean, one-half-mile down.

The 3,028-foot, or over half-a-mile, depth reached by Beebe and Otis Barton in 1934 set a record that stood for the next fifteen years. It was not broken until 1949, off Santa Cruz, California, and then by Barton, who got down to 3,300 feet. Later he reached 4,050 feet. Not till as recently as 1953 in a bathyscaphe was man able to reach the coveted goal of a mile under water.

Beebe and Barton led the parade. When they returned to the harbor of St. George, Bermuda, after their record half-mile dive that August day in 1934, aboard the bathysphere's mother ship *Ready*, a former British Navy craft, Beebe and Barton were saluted by the hoarse siren of the large Furness liner *Monarch of Bermuda*, bound to Bermuda from New York City. Other harbor craft tooted their whistles and set up a din. Mrs. Elswyth Thane Beebe writes me she remembers her own reaction to the end of Dr. Beebe's deep dives. "How I slept that night!" she says.

Dr. Beebe died at almost eighty-five in June 1962. The *Monarch of Bermuda* has been replaced by another Furness ship on the New York–Bermuda run, the *Ocean Monarch*. The men to whom the old *Monarch* growled her salute had achieved the first spectacular breakthrough for mankind in exploring the ocean's depths.

PART
IV

Man Travels Beneath the Sea

Nautilus *Finds the North Pole,* *from Below*

"MEN REMAINED transfixed," wrote Commander William R. Anderson, U.S. Navy, "at the electronic machines clocking our track mile by mile or before the television set on which they would watch the ice passing overhead like beautiful, moving clouds."

Commander Anderson was skipper of the nation's first atomic submarine, the U.S.S. *Nautilus.* The *Nautilus* was cruising 400 feet beneath the surface of the Arctic Ocean. She was beneath ice as much as 65 feet thick, and beneath pressure ridges of ice shown by her TV and her sonar to thrust like knives as much as 100 or 125 feet downward.

She was fast approaching the North Pole. No ship ever had made such a voyage. No ship ever had reached the Pole.

The Arctic Ocean, five times the size of the Mediterranean and twice the area of the United States, was—until U.S. nuclear submarines started exploring it—almost unknown. It has a cover of ice. Commander Anderson described it: "Ice in huge chunks and floes, ranging greatly in size and thickness, grinding one upon the other. . . . Here and there are leads, or cracks in the ice, and polynyas . . . Arctic lagoons." The ice pack, he said, "is in almost constant motion." The Arctic he found "desolate, cold, barren, inhospitable."

He also found it full of unanswered questions. One that Commander Anderson asked himself was: "Can the *Nautilus* make it across the top of the world?" Other basic questions were: How thick is the ice? How deep is the water? Do icebergs, with their deadly, deep keels, drift through the pack? Was there water enough between the ice and the sea floor to slip the *Nautilus* through?

His fathometers would bounce sound off the bottom and tell Commander Anderson how deep the water below the submarine was. A new kind of fathometer, or overhead sonar, that looks upward instead of down showed him the distance of the ice above. This ice-detecting apparatus, as it is called, was the invention of Dr. Waldo Lyon, a physicist at the U.S. Navy Electronics Laboratory in San Diego. Dr. Lyon was traveling aboard the *Nautilus* to help make sure his overhead sonar was functioning at its most efficient. He was senior scientist aboard.

Dr. Lyon had seen the need for his invention when he had worked with submarines during World War II. After the war, U.S. submarines (not nuclear ones, however) had made limited runs under the edge of the Arctic ice, using his upward-looking sonar.

The U.S. Navy, in fact, had been trying to find out how to navigate beneath the Arctic ice for many years before the trip of the *Nautilus* to the Pole. Sir Hubert Wilkins, the British Antarctic explorer, had pointed the way. In a battery-driven (beneath the surface), diesel-driven (on the surface) submarine, handed down to him by the U.S. Navy, Sir Hubert in 1931 planned to puddle-jump beneath the Arctic ice from one polynya, or lagoon, in the ice to another. He planned to surface in each polynya and there recharge the batteries for the next short hop. He had no upward-looking sonar to measure the ice above him. Instead he had inverted sled runners atop his sub (also christened the *Nautilus*), so that the submarine would not be harmed by the underside of the ice.

By August 1931, Sir Hubert had reached the edge of the ice pack between Spitzbergen and Greenland. He made several attempts to skid beneath the ice. Trouble beset him. He lost the stern planes of his *Nautilus*. This made controlling the ship or diving difficult.

Frost formed inside the hull. The crew got cold. The crew got cold on the idea of sailing under the ice, too. Sir Hubert gave up his attempt.

During World War II, several German submarines scampered under the edges of the ice pack when they were avoiding Allied antisubmarine groups. Later, the U.S. Navy icebreaker *Burton Island,* with her fathometers, charted the bottom of some of the Arctic Ocean, and provided some figures on depth that would help Commander Anderson in the *Nautilus.*

In 1948 Commander Skip Palmer took the *Carp,* a diesel-and-battery submarine, on a trip today regarded as the Kitty Hawk of polar submarining. He sailed the *Carp* on the surface till he was 50 miles inside the ice pack. There he found a lagoon about a mile in diameter. From this bit of open water he took *Carp* under the ice. While beneath it, he checked Waldo Lyon's ice detector, then experimental. Then he returned to the lagoon and surfaced. At last man had shown that he could sail in a submarine beneath the ice and get up again in one of the patches of open water.

In 1952 the U.S. submarine *Redfish,* another diesel-and-battery, not atomic-powered, submersible, used Dr. Lyon's overhead sonar to add to *Carp*'s record. *Redfish* stayed under the ice eight hours.

Nautilus, under Commander Anderson, with her nuclear power, was trying to do much, much more. She had the apparent capability to do a great deal. Her reactor had been designed and supervised by Vice Admiral Hyman G. Rickover, the naval officer who, after the first atom bombs fell, set out to make atomic energy perform the task of propelling a submarine. What he did led to today's nuclear submarines. It also led to nuclear carriers, cruisers, and frigates (in 1965 we had one of each, with a second frigate being built). The *Nautilus* was built by the Electric Boat Division of General Dynamics. Her reactor was built by Westinghouse, a job Westinghouse since has repeated many times as the nuclear fleet has grown. *Nautilus* is 320 feet long, 28 feet in draft. Since she doesn't have to carry great amounts of diesel fuel, her crew has more living space than the crews of submarines usually have. When she first headed for sea from Electric Boat, on January 25, 1955, she sent the famous message, "Underway on nuclear power."

On her tests the *Nautilus* performed spectacularly, but not necessarily as planned. On a speed trial, she nosed right into a trawler's net, quickly was hauling the trawler, in the wrong direction, at 20 knots. The trawler captain was upset. Once Captain Eugene P. Wilkinson, *Nautilus'* first skipper, was heading for Puget Sound and Seattle, Washington. Puget Sound was crowded with small boats. It looked like a traffic jam. So Captain Wilkinson entered the sound submerged. Only his periscope was up. When he surfaced, he was almost alongside the pier. "Seldom," said Commander Anderson, "in my days of submarining had I seen anything to equal that maneuver."

Nautilus' first trip under the Arctic ice, from the Atlantic side, did not reach the Pole. It gave Commander Anderson a chance to become familiar with Dr. Lyon's underice sonar, and to look, through his periscope, at the ice. "A diver's light, a powerful lamp," Anderson said, "we had mounted topside so that we could illuminate the underside of the ice for periscope observation."

At first Commander Anderson was dangerously innocent about what the ice-detecting apparatus showed: "We noticed, for example," Commander Anderson says, "that we would get an occasional dip in the pen, indicating the ice was, perhaps, 50 or more feet thick. We dismissed these dips as 'ghosts,' or imperfect returns from the sonar. In actuality, they were not ghosts. They were deep-hanging pressure ridges, dangerous and deadly to our operation. In other words, the ice was much thicker, the pressure ridges much deeper, than we thought."

He took his first look upward at the Arctic Ocean ice. "After we had become adjusted to the sensation of cruising in our silent, frigid world, I felt I would like to take a firsthand look at the ice, so I ordered the ship brought up and slowly raised the periscope. The water was grayish and not at all dark, as the sunlight filtered through the ice. The floodlight we had mounted topside was unnecessary. I turned the field of the periscope up, bringing my eye, through magnification, within a few feet of the underside of the floes, which appeared to be scudding overhead like gray clouds. It was a fascinating but eerie experience. In fact, it was a little unnerving. Since there was nothing from a scientific standpoint to be gained by this, I put the scope back down and tactfully suggested that the curious find something else to do. It was much better watching the ice on sonar."

"Solid sonar constant 900 yards ahead," the conning officer, on one occasion, reported. *Nautilus,* moving fast, turned quickly. The contact: a large fish, shark, or whale.

Commander Anderson found a polynya. He tried to surface in this ice-water lagoon. He ran his periscopes up—*Nautilus* had two —rammed them into the ice, and seriously damaged them. They had struck what apparently was an unseen small block of ice. When *Nautilus* came to the surface of a polynya, three sailors, in a howling wind, used hydraulic jacks to bend the No. 1 periscope back into proper shape. They were John Krawczyk, Robert Scott, and John McGovern. Two others of the crew, Richard T. Bearden and John B. Kurrus, worked twelve hours on the bridge, in a gale, to weld the scope's barrel, which had split open. There were no instruction books on how to do it, so, in the midst of the Arctic storm, said Bearden later, "we ran into many problems of technique. We talked it over as we went along, developing the procedure bit by bit." Another sailor, Jimmy Youngblood, worked out a way to run a hose from the vacuum pumps and apply suction to the periscope barrel and thus create a vacuum that would allow a charge of dry nitrogen gas (which prevents optical fogging) to be shot through a periscope fitting. The result was that the No. 1 periscope, at least, was almost perfect. "It was," said Commander Anderson, "the most amazing repair job at sea I had ever seen."

On this trip from the Atlantic, the *Nautilus* reached a point 180 miles from the North Pole before turning back. She had not been ordered to the Pole; she had been exploring beneath the ice cap.

It took her two attempts from the Pacific to make the voyage no sailor ever had made before: across the Arctic from the Pacific to the Atlantic—and, en route, to cross the North Pole.

The tightest squeeze the *Nautilus* ever was in came on the first effort, and forced her back. She had passed through Bering Strait north into the Chukchi Sea, between Alaska and Siberia. The sea was shallow. The sonar showed ice above. She cleared by five feet, Commander Anderson said, "a mass of ice big enough to supply a 100-pound block to every man, woman, and child in the United States." The sub became sandwiched between ice and muck with only a few feet to spare. "We changed our cruising depth by inches," Anderson said. *Nautilus* could not get through, turned around.

Two months later, on July 23, 1958, *Nautilus* left Oahu, Hawaii, for her second attempt to reach the North Pole. An aerial survey had been made of the Arctic ice. The squeeze in the Chukchi Sea this time was not so tight. *Nautilus,* using a different route, got through. Her sonarmen picked up weird sounds made by a school of walrus. Finally, north of Point Barrow, Alaska, her officers and men established their position by radar sweeps, then headed for the Barrow Sea valley, their deep-water gateway to the Arctic. "As we planed below the surface," said Anderson, "I said to myself: This is it. Let's go, go, go!"

Very few men slept as the ship neared the North Pole. "I did not—could not—sleep," Anderson wrote. "I wandered restlessly about the ship, occasionally taking a peep through the periscope. I was surprised on these observations to see phosphorescent streaks in the water. This is a phenomenon common in tropic waters. It seemed unusual to me to find these streaks in water so cold that the outside of our engine room seawater pipes were covered with thick layers of rime ice."

At 11:15 P.M. eastern daylight time, Sunday, August 3, 1958, *Nautilus* passed beneath the North Pole.

At that point, the only check on navigating aboard the *Nautilus* was her inertial navigator—compasses were not accurate in the immediate vicinity of the Pole. The inertial navigator, a postwar electronic device, provides a ship with her exact position at all times. "I looked anxiously at Tom Curtis," Anderson said. "He was smiling. The inertial navigator had switched precisely as expected, positively confirming that we had crossed the exact North Pole. Curtis sang out: 'As a matter of fact, Captain, you might say we came so close we pierced the Pole.'

"I stood for a moment in silence, awestruck at what *Nautilus* had achieved. She had blazed a new submerged northwest passage, vastly decreasing the sea-travel time for nuclear submarines from the Pacific to the Atlantic, one that could be used even if the Panama Canal were closed. When and if nuclear-powered cargo submarines are built, the new route would cut 4,900 miles and 13 days off the route from Japan to Europe. *Nautilus* had opened a new era, completely conquered the vast, inhospitable Arctic. Our instruments were, for the first time, compiling an accurate and broad picture of the Arctic basin and its approaches. . . . Lastly, for the first time in history a ship had actually reached the North Pole. And never had so many men—116—been gathered at the Pole at one time."

At the Pole there was a water temperature of 32.4 degrees Fahrenheit. The depth of the ocean was 13,410 feet. Waldo Lyon's ice detector found ice overhead: a pressure ridge reaching down 25 feet.

Without changing her course, *Nautilus,* instead of sailing north, now sailed south. Not till two days later did she find open water to surface in. Her radioman called again and again: "Any U.S. Navy radio station . . ." Finally he got a Navy station in Japan. There was sent to Washington, via Japan, another famous message: "*Nautilus* 90 North." Then the *Nautilus* contacted U.S. Navy radio in Honolulu and repeated the message.

Nautilus left the ice pack, called at Iceland, and sailed on to Britain. The trip across the Arctic—what Commander Anderson called "perhaps the most remarkable voyage in the history of man" —was over, and was successful. Commander Anderson himself is today a Congressman from Tennessee. As a member of the House Committee on Science and Astronautics, he helps keep an eye on our space program.

CHAPTER
15

Skate Comes Up for Air
at the Pole

"THE CLARITY of the water," said Commander James Calvert, U.S. Navy, "and the amount of light were startling." Calvert was cruising 180 feet beneath the surface of the Arctic Ocean in *Skate,* the second U.S. submarine to travel a long way beneath the Arctic ice. She was actually so close behind the *Nautilus* that she was under the ice in 1958 at the same time the *Nautilus* was there.

"At this same depth in the Atlantic," Calvert continued, "the water looks black or at best a dark green, but here the sea was a pale and transparent blue, like the lovely tropical waters off the Bahamas. I hooked my arm over the right handle of the periscope and tugged on it. At this depth—where a periscope is normally not used—it pressed heavily against its supporting bearing and could be turned only with great difficulty. A blob of color came into the field of sight. I turned a knob on the periscope barrel to bring it into focus and found we had company. The ethereal, translucent shape of a jellyfish was swimming near the periscope, gracefully waving his rainbow-colored tentacles in the quiet water of a sea whose surface is forever protected from waves by its cover of ice." The Arctic Ocean is home to the giant among jellyfishes, *Cyanea arctica,* up to 8 feet across, with tentacles up to 200 feet long. They are laden with stingers. "We can only imagine what it would be like to be stung by such a monstrous coelenterate," Ralph Buchsbaum and Lorus J. Milne, American zoologists, comment.

The *Nautilus* answered the question of whether a nuclear submarine could cross the Arctic Ocean. The *Skate* now had the next question to answer: Could a submarine find polynyas, those openings in the ice, frequently? Frequently enough to help make the Arctic Ocean useful as a vast base for nuclear submarines? Nuclear submarines, including those that carry missiles, can stay down a long time—months—without needing fresh air. It would be, however, desirable from the point of view of the crew of the submarine to surface, to let the men breathe fresh air and to ventilate the ship, and to allow the crew a romp on the ice. Furthermore, a nuclear submarine above the surface in a polynya can erect her radio antennas and communicate with the world. A missile-carrying submarine could launch her rockets from a polynya, then could duck back under the ice and be impossible to find, let alone destroy.

The *Skate* proved that polynyas were reasonably plentiful, and could be found and used. She was looking for a polynya when Commander Calvert was impressed with the clear water. She found one, and came up. A companion came up with her. "Slowly climbing out of the water and up onto the ice was a full-grown polar bear," Calvert said. "He shook himself like a wet dog and gazed curiously at this intruder in his domain." He showed no fear.

Nautilus, Skate, and other U.S. submarines that have opened up the Arctic depths have done so despite continuous and real dangers. Because U.S. submarines in the Arctic so far have been accompanied by good fortune rather than *Thresher*-like tragedy, the dangers they have overcome in writing a completely new chapter in exploring the depths of the sea are sometimes overlooked. Among them are:

> *Possible mechanical failure.* If a nuclear plant should stop, for any reason, under the ice, the lives of the crew would depend on restarting it quickly. Battery power could not be used long enough to escape from the ice unless the ship was near the edge of the pack. Auxiliary diesel power would require much oxygen, not available

unless the submarine could surface, which would depend on the thickness of the ice.

"If we should fail [to restart the nuclear engines]," wrote Skipper James Calvert of *Skate,* "we could find a cold and airless tomb."

Possible weather disasters. Up for fresh air in a polynya in the Arctic, our submarine skippers have been dismayed to see the polynya shrink and the ice close in on their ships. A submarine could either be crushed or damaged by the ice and could only be saved by a quick dive when thus shut in.

Possible underwater collisions. A submarine is much more vulnerable underwater to a collision than is a surface ship. An egg, because of its shape, can go deep before it shatters from the pressure of the sea; a submarine likewise. The egg, however, will fracture if given a light blow. So will a submarine at depth. So special care must be taken to avoid bottoms of icebergs or tops of undersea mountains or a collision with anything else.

Possible blindness. The *Nautilus* damaged her periscopes when she struck a stray block of ice.

Possible damage when rising through the Arctic surface ice. If the submarine comes up too fast, the hull may rupture. If she comes up too slowly, there may not be force enough to break through the ice.

In addition, there is in the Arctic, and out of sight of the sky as submariners often are, the continual problem of knowing where you are. Like *Nautilus, Skate* had a newfangled inertial navigator installed. "It was an impressive sight," Commander Calvert wrote, "with its mysterious green-glowing tubes, banks of dials and meters, and rows of flashing dots which, when properly counted, revealed the information stored up in its mechanical brain. How does it work? Well, gyroscopes are important here, too. A series of them stabilize a platform deep in the heart of the system. This platform tends to remain fixed in space—not just in relation to the *Skate* or the earth, but also in relation to the entire universe, to the fixed stars. Delicate devices sense any attempt to move the plaform out of its position, whether due to the movement (speed, route, drift) of the *Skate* or the motion of the earth. By sensing, and remembering, the forces that disturb the platform, the system and its computers can determine the position of the *Skate* as she moves about the globe, whether at the equator or under the frozen ice pack at the North Pole."

The crew at first did not view the inertial navigator with unlimited confidence. One of them taped a Boy Scout compass on top of the big machine so he would know which way was north. To implement the inertial navigator, another sailor provided the ship's navigators with an Esso road map, with the way to the North Pole indicated upon it.

There is one problem, not as acute as some of the others, but to men just as uncomfortable, that nuclear submarines help solve. "I think," said Commander Calvert, "the most striking and distinct difference from any other sort of seagoing is that one is free, completely free, from the surface of the sea.

"The ancient curse of the seagoer is that strangely nauseating motion imparted to ships by the surface of the sea. For centuries, sailors (especially Navy men) have denied its existence; most would rather choke than admit that it affects them. But it does. Even men who have gone to sea all their lives and have long since got over any trace of seasickness, no matter what the weather, know the discomfort and fatigue that come from the surface of the sea. The British have an expressive term for it: sea-weariness. And no one knows better what this means than those who take ordinary submarines to sea. Small and low in the water, they are miserable in rough weather and uncomfortable all the time. Forced to remain on or near the surface to get the air which their diesel engines consume in such huge quantities, they are always affected by the motion of the water.

"In the *Skate,* however, we are breaking the long-established rules of sea travel. Our throbbing turbines receive their power from a source that has no need of oxygen or any other ingredient of the atmosphere. Traveling 300 feet below the surface day after day, we are almost devoid of any sense of motion. Only the almost imperceptible vibration of our propellers reminds us we are moving. Consequently, to walk through the ship is like passing through a small, highly concentrated, self-sufficient city built deep underground, with mechanical instruments as its only link with the outside world."

The *Skate* set a course for the North Pole. Her fathometer traced the floor of the North Eurasian Basin, 12,000 feet down. "Imagine," said Calvert, "a kitchen matchstick suspended about 2 inches below the ceiling of a 10-foot-high room. The ceiling would be the ice, the floor the bottom of the sea, and the humble matchstick our submarine."

She reached the Pole, the second submarine ever to do so, on August 12, 1958—only nine days after *Nautilus* had been there. *Skate* did not surface. Leaving the Pole, the fathometer showed she was over the foothills of the Lomonosov Ridge. This is a mountain range under the Arctic Ocean discovered after World War II by the Russians, from a camp on the ice. The ridge, confirmed by other soundings as well as *Skate*'s, runs from Greenland to the New Siberian Islands.

Skate now had a difficult task: to locate the Americans in their own camp on a floating ice island, at a station called Alfa. Halfway between the Pole and Alaska, *Skate* found a polynya and came to the surface. The ice fields were dotted with pools of melting water, as they normally are in August. "These blue jewels were scattered in every direction over the ermine white of the floes," Calvert said. He figured he was 30 miles from Ice Station Alfa. His radioman made contact with Alfa (call letters: ICE). Alfa said the station would run an outboard motor continuously in the polynya nearest the camp. Louis Kleinlein, *Skate*'s senior sonarman, thought he could pick up the sound five miles away.

Skate submerged under the ice, headed for Alfa, heard the outboard, passed the station, returned, nosed around, heard the outboard again—and eventually surfaced not far from some small huts, a high radio antenna, a radar dome, and a pole flying an American flag.

The men at Alfa were from the Lamont Geological Observatory of Columbia University, the University of Washington, and the Air Force. They were hospitable, and gave the *Skate* crew some polar-bear meat for a future dinner, but the *Skate*'s cook managed to lose it. They showed a flashbulb picture taken 10,000 feet down of a large, uncovered boulder, probably dropped off a melting ice island. The ice began to move, and the polynya in which *Skate* was tied up began to shrink; the ice was closing in. When the polynya was half its former size, *Skate* submerged—and was gone.

Skate next mapped the Lomonosov Ridge. Submerged, she followed it back toward the Pole, zigzagging so that her fathometer could get as complete a picture as possible. She surfaced in another polynya. The top water of a polynya, Calvert explains, is warm; then comes a layer of cold water. "When we looked down," he said, "we could see tiny white Arctic shrimp crawling along at the surface of this cold layer as if it were the bottom of the sea. The clarity of the water was startling. The shrimp were as clearly visible as though they had been floating on air."

During several surfacings, something clouded over the periscope. Calvert decided what was responsible: diatoms. These are the most common tiny plants in the sea, part of the phytoplankton. They grow in the summer in the top layer of water in a polynya, then sink to the bottom of the layer. They may be eaten by shrimp.

Skate returned to the Pole. Counting the crossing by *Nautilus,* there had been three visits there by U.S. submarines in two weeks. "A regular service," John Medaglia called it. *Skate* then sailed two miles away and traveled a 12-mile circle around the Pole in an hour in order to get detailed soundings of the area. It was probably the fastest trip around the world ever made.

Skate returned to Boston, but was back in the Arctic in March to see what could be done during the winter there. She had added powerful floodlights to light up the ice from underneath and a closed-circuit television system. The camera was embedded in the deck in a watertight container.

On her first dive under the ice she traveled 190 miles without locating a single opening in the wintertime Arctic Ocean covering. One morning, Calvert said, "I walked over to the television screen. It was getting light above and the ice was once more visible. However, here was quite a different picture from that of the drifting blocks of yesterday. Now huge black patches of floe ice could be seen, outlined in the dim light which filtered through the thinner ice surrounding them. It was rather like looking up through a gigantic fruit Jell-O salad. There was no sign of a break in this translucent ceiling."

Skate headed again for the Pole. Waldo Lyon's ice detector and television camera watched for patches of thin ice. "Suddenly," said Calvert, "the screen was flooded with fish. . . . Individually they were very small—no more than 8 inches long—but their numbers seemed countless. Men came from all over the ship to watch the show. Here we were, 400 feet below the surface and less than 300 miles from the North Pole—what sort of fish could they be? No one could be sure, but both Dr. Lyon and Walt Wittman thought they most closely resembled ordinary North Atlantic herring. The school was enormous. On we went, mile after mile, and the sea appeared full of fish. . . .

"The hypnotically undulating pattern was rudely broken when a huge black shape shot suddenly through the picture, jaws agape and eye flashing. And that's about all the description I can give. All of us were watching closely at the time but whatever it was came and went too swiftly for identification. It was apparent that he was up to no good, and at first we all thought it was some sort of predatory fish. Afterward it occurred to us that it might also have been a seal, but whether or not seals can go that deep is not known . . . suddenly the little fish were gone.

"Who knows how many other displays of nature we missed beneath the Arctic ice simply for lack of eyes to see them?"

Two hundred miles from the Pole, Commander Calvert stopped *Skate* and raised the periscope. The sea was black; nothing showed through the ice above. "We were," he says, "sealed in."

There was heavy ice right up to the Pole itself. Then, all of a sudden, the ice became thin. *Skate* surfaced. She broke through. Calvert raced up the ladder, through the hatch, onto the bridge. "I was struck," he said, "by the first heavy wind I had ever experienced in the Arctic. It howled and swirled across the open bridge, carrying stinging snow particles which cut like flying sand. Heavy gray clouds hung in the sky; the impression was of a dark and stormy twilight about to fade into night." That was the North Pole in late winter, on March 17, 1959. *Nautilus* had been the first ship to reach the Pole, but had remained submerged and had not stopped. Now there was *Skate,* the first ship in history to come up to the surface at the top of the world.

Skate's men took a walk on the ice. They held a memorial service for Sir Hubert Wilkins, who had died not long before, and sprinkled his ashes in the North Pole wind. They fired a last salute.

Skate had proved something else: She could surface not only in an occasional polynya, but, in the case of the Pole on that day at least, at a predetermined spot. This of course could add greatly to the military value of the Arctic.

One more "first" remained for this trip: In a small polynya, *Skate*'s aqualungers got a chance to swim. In 23-degrees-below-zero weather, they—Dave Boyd, Dick Arnest, Dick Brown, and Sam Hall—put on heavy sponge rubber suits and masks and entered the water. They took water samples but saw only a couple of jellyfish. From the water, they announced it was warm. But as soon as they climbed out, their suits froze, and when they reentered the submarine, they tinkled and crackled as the ice broke and fell off.

Shortly thereafter, *Skate* returned to New London. One of the messages she received was from the Chief of Naval Operations: "Well done. Arleigh Burke." Today Commander Calvert is a rear admiral.

Triton *Sails Submerged* *Around the Globe*

EVERYTHING about U.S.S. *Triton* is big: She is 447½ feet long —more than 100 feet longer than any previous American submarine. She is 37 feet in beam. When she submerges, she displaces 8,000 tons, or about twice as much as any earlier submarine. She has two nuclear reactors, not one. She has two propellers, each 11 feet in diameter. She stands seven stories high. Her sail—the high superstructure atop her hull that carries periscopes and retractable masts for such things as radio antennas—is 74 feet long, or only 20 feet shorter than the Navy's first submarine, the U.S.S. *Holland* of 1900. *Triton*'s size indicates, some observers believe, that the day of freight, tanker, and passenger submarines of large size is not far off.

When *Triton* first put to sea, running down the Thames River from Electric Boat to Long Island Sound, in September, 1959, she seemed destined for something big. She was.

On her first cruise, she traveled around the world. Nuclear power made it possible for her to do so without a refueling stop, and without needing to refuel even when she returned home. But she made her round-the-world voyage with a difference. She made the trip submerged. No submarine had ever tried such a thing. *Triton* had been selected for two reasons. Her two nuclear reactors meant that if either broke down, the other could complete the voyage.

And her size meant that she could carry the supplies and scientific equipment necessary.

At that, at least one thing was in short supply: bunk space. She had 183 Navy men and scientists aboard for the trip. There were not enough bunks. So Captain Edward L. Beach, U.S. Navy, her skipper (the author of *Run Silent, Run Deep* and *Submarine!*), added two hammocks. After all, Horatio Nelson, the great hero of Britain's Royal Navy, had slept in a hammock, and so had John Paul Jones.

Captain Beach failed to get his point across. His crew avoided the hammocks; no one learned to sleep in one.

One object of the *Triton*'s trip was to gather oceanographic and gravitational data in a continuous circuit around the globe. This would provide a solid line about which information was complete, and thus establish a kind of base line of knowledge concerning the sea.

The start and finish of *Triton*'s voyage were St. Peter and St. Paul's Rocks in mid-Atlantic, about 50 miles from the equator.

These black rocks are only 1,400 by 700 feet. The highest, 60 feet above sea level, is always wet with spray. Insects, birds, and spiders are the only living things upon the rocks. "As we approached the islet," Captain Beach said, "it presented varying shapes. [A] white spot looked at first like the sail of a ship, then like a sun-kissed minaret, finally like a huge bird cage. At last I recognized it as the structure of the abandoned lighthouse. The upper parts of the rocks were pure white from bird droppings, and the lower levels, as we approached, were a sort of brownish black, ceaselessly washed by the waves. The sea was relatively smooth, yet there was considerable surf breaking in and among the rocks, foaming madly like a miniature waterfall one minute, stopping abruptly the next and reversing itself. As we came closer, we could distinguish a great number of granitelike outcroppings scattered about everywhere, and there were large numbers of sea birds." The rocks are exposed summits of the 10,000-mile-long mid-Atlantic

Ridge; other summits of the ridge are Jan Mayen Island, the Azores, Tristan da Cunha, Ascension, Gough, and Bouvet Islands.

From St. Peter and St. Paul's Rocks, the *Triton* went around Cape Horn, at the southernmost tip of South America, across the Pacific, past Guam and the Philippines and the East Indies, across the Indian Ocean, around the Cape of Good Hope, at the southern tip of Africa, and back northwest up the Atlantic to St. Peter and St. Paul's Rocks. She then cruised past Cadíz, Spain, to present a plaque to Spain: Her voyage had almost exactly duplicated the trip of Magellan, the sailor for Spain of four centuries ago whose ship was the first one around the world. Magellan did not himself make it back; he died on the way.

Soon after she began her round-the-world trip, *Triton* had become handicapped. Of all things, her fathometer—fathometers show the ocean's depth—conked out, and was useless for much of the voyage. This was particularly a handicap for an undersea trip. Because they must, *Triton*'s crew and Captain Beach learned how to use their sonar to measure depth, at least in shallow waters. They were pleased when it proved sensitive enough to outline a big boulder on the bottom. It showed nothing over the Philippine Trench, one of the deepest places in the sea. "I remember looking with interest at the repeater scope of our search sonar," Captain Beach wrote. "We were in a sea of nothingness. The limits of the huge trench were well beyond the range of sonar, the bottom so far away as to be like a void."

Triton's most chilling moment came when she fell through a hole in the sea. She was in the Lombok Strait, approaching the Indian Ocean. Through her periscope Captain Beach saw a ridge of water several feet high, caused perhaps by the meeting of a warm current from the Lombok Strait with a cool current of the Indian Ocean. The diving officer had trouble maintaining periscope depth. The ship, despite his efforts, drifted downward. In 40 seconds, she had fallen to a depth of 125 feet.

"It was as though we had hit a hole in the water which acted on us as a downdraft would act on an aircraft," Captain Beach said. "Under the circumstances, *Triton*'s size, tremendously strong hull and great power pretty well eliminated any danger, especially since we had tight control of the ship at all times; but the situation of a wartime submarine with a weaker hull and only battery power must have been less comfortable.

"I had experienced changes in water density many times before, but never one of this magnitude, nor this suddenness. There had been wartime reports of British submarines in the Mediterranean having somewhat the same experience, and some of the hard-to-believe stories of the period laid heavy losses in the 'Med' to this phenomenon."

Back at St. Peter and St. Paul's Rocks, Captain Beach entered in his log: "First submerged circumnavigation of the world is now complete." From the rocks to the rocks he had sailed 26,723 nautical miles in 60 days and 21 hours. *Triton* went back home to New London. She received the Presidential Unit Citation from President Eisenhower.

U.S. nuclear submarines have continued to make other outstanding trips.

In February, 1960, the *Sargo* poked through three feet of ice to surface at the North Pole. She was the third U.S. submarine to get there, preceded by *Nautilus* and *Skate*. She had traveled 2,744 miles under the ice in 14 days, 21 hours. She showed (as had the *Skate* before her) that the U.S. Navy now knows how to surface through ice during the Arctic winter.

In September, 1960, the *Seadragon,* Commander George P. Steele II, reached Honolulu after negotiating a northwest passage across the Arctic (the Parry Channel through the Canadian archipelago).

In August 1962, the *Seadragon,* coming from the west coast, and *Skate,* from the east coast, met under the Arctic ice pack, headed for the North Pole, and together surfaced there.

For at least a thousand years the Arctic ice cap has been a glittering magnet for great explorers. There were the Vikings, who were the only sailors of their day (before A.D. 1000) who could navigate by sun and stars and so sail out of sight of land. There was Eric the Red, who colonized Greenland. There was Eric's son, Leif Ericsson, probably born in Iceland, who may have reached the North American coast (according to a fifteenth-century map that Yale University analyzed in 1965) near today's Hudson Strait and the Gulf of St. Lawrence. And then there were Martin Frobisher, John and Sebastian Cabot, Sir Francis Drake, John Davys, Henry Hudson, William Baffin, Willem Barents, F. W. Beechey (who discovered Point Barrow, the most northerly point of Alaska), Roald Amundsen, Vilhjalmur Stefansson, Sir Francis Leopold McClintock (who made Husky dogs one of the most dependable forms of Arctic transportation before our nuclear submarines), Robert E. Peary, Otto Sverdrup, Peter Freuchen, D. B. MacMillan, Richard E. Byrd, Floyd Bennett, Umberto Nobile (via dirigible), Sir Hubert Wilkins. Today men like Bill Field and Walter Wood explore the Arctic. In 1956 Vice Admiral John M. Will, U.S. Navy, thought he had spotted from the air what no man ever had found— a summertime ice-free northwest passage for surface ships; the next year Her Majesty's Canadian ship *Labrador,* Captain Thomas C. Pullen, and the U.S. Coast Guard's *Storis, Bramble,* and *Spar* made the passage. They sailed through Bellot Strait, 2,000 miles due north of Minneapolis and St. Paul. Other famous Coast Guard ships, *Bear, Mackinac, Eastwind, Northwind, Westwind,* made annual voyages taking medicine and supplies to Eskimos and Americans in the Arctic.

The remarkable records made by these men and ships and by many others have been added to by American nuclear submarines. The Arctic, the only ocean not crossed regularly by ships, has been opened up and made to serve man by the United States' nuclear submarines.

Our Submarines Go
Deeper, Faster, Farther

"SHALL WE FLY?" Lieutenant Commander Jon L. Boyes, U.S. Navy, early one summer morning in 1956 was addressing eight officers and visitors around his wardroom table. I was one of the visitors.

The question asked at that place seemed startling. For Commander Boyes was captain of the U.S. submarine *Albacore*. As he spoke, the *Albacore* was cruising 100 feet beneath the surface of the Atlantic.

But actually the question, to Boyes at least, was normal. For the *Albacore* was one of the world's fastest submarines. In speed and maneuverability she was at the time outperforming the atompowered *Nautilus*. The *Albacore* was so fast under water that her maneuvers might well be called a flight, and words and terms of aviation were used to describe our trip. Today the *Albacore* remains one of the world's fastest submarines.

Boyes and the rest of us went to the *Albacore*'s flight-control center (another aviation term).

Here, inside the hull beneath the sail (formerly called the conning tower), sit two pilots and a flight-control engineer—not helmsmen. In anchored-down leather seats like those of airliner pilots, they control the bow planes and stern planes (used for diving and climbing) and the rudders. There are two rudders: one at the stern, and one just behind the sail for easier, quicker turns. "The turning rate of this monster," Skipper Boyes told me, "is faster than a jet plane's."

The controls themselves are borrowed from aviation: sticks with steering wheels atop them. There is no large wheel of the kind ordinary ships have, for the *Albacore* is not an ordinary ship.

The word went to all hands over the public address system: "Now hear this. We will be taking angles and heels now."

Crew and visitors prepared themselves for rapid movements of the ship. The pilots and flight-control engineer fastened their safety belts. The rest of us located the nearest means of bracing ourselves, by holding handrails or overhead straps exactly like those for straphangers on streetcars or buses. Several men heard the announcement while in the ship's heads. They promptly emerged. A john is no place to be while the *Albacore* takes angles and heels.

Boyes spoke to his maneuvering room: "Make turns for 18 knots."

He next addressed his senior pilot. Aboard the *Albacore,* as on an airliner, this is an officer, Lt. Theodore F. Davis, USN, the ship's executive officer.

"Your ceiling is one hundred feet," Boyes told Davis. "Your floor will be three-five-zero."

The maneuvering room reported turns for 18 knots. A minute later, Boyes ordered Davis: "Go to floor."

Pilot Davis moved his stick. Instantly, but with a silky smoothness, the ship pointed her nose down, way down, and almost plummeted for her floor—not the bottom of the sea, but the depth Skipper Boyes had specified: 350 feet beneath the surface.

The needle on the depth gauge spun around as the *Albacore* dived downward.

Next Skipper Boyes had the *Albacore* ascend, descend, twist, and turn as she approached an imaginary target. The *Albacore* speeded up. Boyes's orders to his pilot sounded like something you'd expect to hear in a dogfight miles above the earth: "Peel over to the left," or, "right ascent to the ceiling."

It was quiet down there. A book fell to the deck. A coffee spoon rattled. Otherwise everything was so well secured that there was no clatter. The battery-powered motors only hummed.

Officers and crew were quiet. They were concentrating on their jobs. One man chewed a dead cigar stub. They did not talk. Some were watching the skipper. Besides the orders I have put down, Boyes gave other commands by hand signal. This eliminated the possibility of somebody hearing wrong and made things safer.

We visitors were quiet because we were struck dumb. Our eyes were popping. Our mouths were gaping. We were, it had dawned on us, among the first men in history to fly underwater. But that was not all: The flight of the *Albacore* demonstrated in a short few minutes that we were aboard a ship that would revolutionize submarine warfare. There were two reasons, both of them obvious.

The first is her speed. Eighteen knots is faster than most of the world's merchant ships can travel on the surface. But submarines in the past have been slower still. Our subs that wreaked havoc on Japanese shipping during World War II and the German subs that did the same to Allied ships in the Atlantic cruised beneath the sea at far slower speeds. Often, therefore, they had to lie in wait for a merchant ship all day.

Yet the *Albacore* beneath the surface can travel faster than most of the ships upon it. She can chase and catch a surface vessel—and remain hidden while she does. Not only that, but a sub of her class can circle most ships, take her time, and fire a torpedo at her convenience. If she misses, she can try again. "The *Albacore,*" says Boyes, "has moved us out of the one-shot system."

The second is her maneuverability. Because the *Albacore* flies through the depths of the sea, turning or zigzagging while diving or climbing, she can outmaneuver that traditional enemy of submarines, the destroyer. She can go from dead in the water to full speed ahead in much less time than a destroyer. She can turn in a fraction of the room a destroyer needs.

Slower submarines of the past, when attacked by destroyers, had to lie still on the bottom and pray that the depth charges would miss. The *Albacore* never will have to.

She will never in fact have to flee from a destroyer at all. "We'll stay in there and slug it out," Lt. Jack D. Venable, USN, the *Albacore*'s operations officer and navigator, said to me. "The thing is," said Skipper Boyes, "we never have to go on the defensive. We have the maneuverability and the speed to be attacking, always attacking.

"Going over onto the defensive always worried me"—Boyes is a submariner of many years' experience—"and always to attack makes me happy, very happy."

Boyes asked me to take over the controls from Pilot Davis. Another officer told me my job was to keep the *Albacore* on an even keel, which you do by moving the stick slightly forward or back, as necessary, depending on whether she's nosing down or up.

The whole feel of the sea and all its power comes to you through the stick and the wheel. You take hold, and you now try for several minutes to keep the ship on an even keel. She, meanwhile, goes first down, then up.

You are not, an officer informs you, anywhere near as good as the automatic pilot.

If we as visitors were amazed at what we saw, it can be said that the performance of the *Albacore* surprised the Navy also. To achieve the *Albacore,* the Navy set out, as long ago as 1947, to design an ideal underwater hull. To get the right shape, the Navy tested 25 hulls, 7 to 25 feet long, at the Experimental Towing Tank of Stevens Institute, Hoboken, New Jersey, and at the David Taylor Model Basin, Washington, D.C. A whale shape appeared best. A small model of this shape was tested, to study air drag and lift, in a wind tunnel at Langley Air Force Base, Virginia. Then the Navy decided to build a full-size, 203-foot-long, 1,800-ton model.

That model is the *Albacore* herself: a working model that set speed and maneuverability records.

Albacore was the Navy's first submarine of advanced hydrodynamic design. Her hull was shaped for the greatest possible speed and performance underwater. Nobody cared what she would do on the surface. And she doesn't do much—she's slow on the surface, and full of rock-'n'-roll.

She has been called the world's first true submersible—i.e., her streamlined whale shape is the best configuration to operate in the depths.

Her engines are ordinary submarine engines, not nuclear reactors: diesel for surface travel, battery-powered for beneath the sea. She must come up often to charge her batteries. And, unlike the nuclear submarines, she must refuel regularly and often.

The lessons taught by the speed and maneuverability of the *Albacore* were at once applied by the Navy.

Many of our nuclear submarines today have *Albacore*-shaped hulls. All of our submarines since *Skipjack* are variations of *Albacore*'s hull form.

Suppose our antisubmarine, whale-shaped submarines—each as agile as the *Albacore*—were formed into a wolf pack. What such a pack could do to a task force or convoy or other submarines staggers the imagination. The only submersible that could hold its own against them would be another submarine with similar capability.

Even today's Polaris missile submarines have modified bulbous hulls and, like the *Albacore,* single screws. They are, the Navy believes, ships that can get there "fustest with the mostest"—ships that roam the oceans of the world at will, nuclear ships that can launch nuclear weapons against enemy land targets.

Those land targets can be 2,500 miles inland. The Polaris A3 missile can travel that far.

With its long range, the Polaris, developed under Vice-Admiral William Francis Raborn, Jr., has made the Navy a power on land as well as at sea. The A3 is the last Polaris missile we will make, since it is planned to replace Polarises with new Poseidons. Either missile can be fired from beneath the surface of the sea.

The first time this was done was on July 20, 1960, when the submerged nuclear submarine *George Washington* launched a Polaris missile. This means the Navy knows how to strike a match underwater. How it is done is still a military secret.

The Polaris subs of 1965–70 are far less vulnerable than surface ships, and not only because of their speed and maneuverability. Like the *Albacore,* they are able to dive deep. They can dive beneath water layers of different temperatures and thus find hiding places in the sea that bounce back the enemy's sonar waves and keep the sonar from finding them. For this reason they are hard or impossible to locate. And since they are dispersed over the oceans of the world and are always moving, they are immune to the sudden, Pearl Harbor-type of attack. An enemy cannot knock them out with a single blow. All in all, the Polaris submarines may be the most effective weapon at present in keeping the peace.

Our total submarine fleet in 1965 was 104 nuclear and conventional attack submarines and 30 fleet ballistic (missile) submarines. The *Benjamin Franklin,* our thirtieth Polaris submarine, joined the fleet October 22, 1965. The *Kamehameha,* our thirty-first, named for a Hawaiian king, successfully completed her sea trials off San Francisco in November 1965. Great Britain in 1964 commissioned her first nuclear submarine, the *Dreadnought;* her second is to be the *Valiant;* her third will be *Churchill.*

Albacore's round whale-shaped hull both speeds her up through the water and offers good resistance to the high pressures at great depths. "The whale," John Crompton wrote in *The Living Sea,* "is as beautifully streamlined as any fish." The *Albacore*'s performance showed that the whale was pretty well designed for any underwater travel.

One result of the design of the *Albacore* is that she scoots along even without her propeller pushing. Once, when her screw had been removed, she was being towed beneath the surface by a vessel upon it. The surface ship stopped; the *Albacore* slid right on past and ahead of her.

"Look at this stubby, round hull with big fins sticking out of it at odd angles," Skipper Boyes said as he showed me over his ship. "That, I believe, is the fashion of the future. The style is going to be short and plump."

Boyes means, he says, that not only will future submarines look like the *Albacore*. He thinks that eventually passenger ships, freighters, tankers, tugs, and other vessels will, too. He believes the day will come when most vessels will be built to travel beneath the surface—not upon it. This, of course, assumes that men will have learned to cope with those great undersea waves, and that accurate maps of the depths showing seamounts, ridges, slopes, and reefs are in existence—at least for the shipping lanes, if not for the 95 percent of the depths that are unmapped so far.

If the day of submersible liners and tankers does come, and men and cargoes travel under the sea in ships patterned after the *Albacore,* it would be the greatest change in ships since the switch from sail to steam. It could mean 80-knot, 35-hour voyages from New York to London. Though a long way off, experts believe these are achievable.

It would mean also fewer disrupted schedules. Today even the *Queen Mary* and the *United States* sometimes lose a day or more, due to storms. In the day of undersea liners, says Boyes, you'll set your depth and course once and let the automatic pilot take you right across the ocean.

If that day comes, as I can tell you from my own trip aboard the *Albacore,* you'll fly through the sea with the greatest of ease. I felt less motion as she moved through the depths than in any liner, small boat, plane, train, and car I ever traveled in. Even vibration is almost eliminated.

Only when an undersea liner climbs, turns, or descends might it be necessary for you to hang on or watch your step. But a passenger submarine presumably would not make rapid twists any more often than a commercial airliner does. But it must first be proved that a ship can be propelled underwater with less horsepower and at less cost than on the surface.

"The *Albacore,*" said the Navy's Bureau of Ships, "is the first submarine to be constructed where this condition does exist."

Commander (now Captain) Boyes, relieved as captain of the *Albacore,* is today assigned to the office of the Secretary of Defense. Commander Theodore F. Davis is on the staff of the Commander Submarine Force, U.S. Pacific Fleet. Lieutenant Commander Jack D. Venable is serving aboard the U.S.S. *Alstede.*

Albacore's home port still is Portsmouth, New Hampshire, where I boarded her. And her influence continues.

The necessities of national defense are here now, as they always are. "Our national interest, indeed our national survival," says Warren G. Magnuson, U.S. Senator from Washington, "demands that no foreign power gain dominion either of the oceans or in space." There is no exact public information on the Soviet Union's submarine fleet. It is believed to total around the formidable number of 500 submarines—several times as many as Germany had at the start of World War II. The Soviet Union, according to Jane's *All the World's Fighting Ships,* has about 25 nuclear submarines, including a number of missile-carrying subs. Russia also has a nuclear icebreaker, the *Lenin,* a ship that is used for oceanographic research, and is building two more that are expected to be finished in 1971.

Meanwhile, partly due to lessons taught by the *Albacore,* one solid and comforting fact has been established: By far the world's fastest and most capable submarines today do not belong to any possible enemy. They are ours.

PART
V

Man Lives on the Sea Floor

Thirty Days at 205 Feet Down, Three Weeks at 325

AT 5:32 P.M. eastern daylight time on July 20, 1964, four men arrived at their new place to live. It was perhaps not too spacious, but it was new and well equipped. The only unusual thing about it was that it was 190 feet below sea level, on the bottom of the ocean near Bermuda.

The men remained there, working in and outdoors (on the bottom of the sea, that is) for 11 days. Then they returned to the surface.

All were in the Navy: Lester E. Anderson, Gunner's Mate First Class; Robert A. Barth, Chief Quartermaster; Sanders W. Manning, Chief Hospital Corpsman; and Lieutenant Robert E. Thompson, Medical Corps. All were in their thirties, married, with children, and experienced divers.

Their quarters were named Sealab I. Sealab I was a 40-foot-long chamber in which air pressure was kept up to equal that of the surrounding water (86 pounds per square inch). This meant that no water could enter. Sealab I was constructed by the Navy Mine Defense Laboratory, at Panama City, Florida. For the Office of Naval Research, the Bureau of Ships, and the Naval Medical Research Laboratory, sponsors of Sealab, one of the questions to be answered was how men's minds and bodies would function beneath the sea over an extended period of time. Another question was how best men could work on the bottom of the sea outside protective shells like submarines, diving bells, and pressurized suits.

Another question dealt with one of the most aggravating problems in undersea exploration: how to avoid wasting time. No matter how long he stays down, a diver must decompress on returning to the surface. If a diver spends 30 minutes at 190 feet, he must afterward spend more than an hour decompressing.

However, in a longer period of time—24 hours at a depth of 200 feet—a diver's tissues become saturated: he has absorbed all of the breathing gas (the Navy uses a mixture of helium, nitrogen, and oxygen) he can absorb. From then on, no matter how long he remains below, his decompression time will not increase. So it is better to leave men on the bottom for weeks at a time than to have them make frequent dives. For this they need a warm, dry shelter— in this case Sealab I—where they can live when not on the job out on the sea floor.

The four men in Sealab I were the first aquanauts in U.S. history —the first Americans to live in deep water for an extended period. The only men to try to live beneath the sea before them had been Jacques-Yves Cousteau and his associates.

In 1962 in Captain Cousteau's Conshelf I (for continental shelf), a 17-by-18-foot cylinder, two men lived for a week 33 feet down off Marseille, France; divers from Conshelf I went down to 85 feet. In June 1963, in Conshelf II, Cousteau's team (five men) lived for a month 36 feet down; two men stayed a week 90 feet down. They were in the Red Sea in Starfish House. The men living at 90 feet dived to, and worked at, a depth of 165 feet. On a bounce dive (down and right up) they reached 360-plus feet down. They also operated the diving saucer, *Denise* (later used to explore off California) from an underwater garage.

The Navy men of Sealab I made their trip down into the sea inside a diving bell, a small submersible decompression chamber. The trip took about 2 minutes. Sealab I was about 30 miles southwest of Bermuda, and about 300 feet away from the Argus Island research tower maintained by the Navy. Once at the bottom, 192 feet down, the men left their diving bell, stepped out into the sea, then entered their undersea home through one of the two open "manholes" in its floor. The men entered and left Sealab I at all times through these two holes in the floor. Since the air pressure inside Sealab I equaled the surrounding seawater pressure, no locks were required; the sea could not force its way in.

A surface barge, or lighter, the *YFNB-12,* Chief Boatswain William C. Hollingsworth, officer-in-charge, supported the Sealab I men. Aboard the barge there was kept the first log of Americans dwelling on the sea floor. Here in the exact words of Navy men on the *YFNB-12* is an account of how things went for the first Americans to take up residence on the bottom of the sea:

First day

The aquanauts awakened at 7:30 A.M. After eating their breakfast of corned beef, crackers, and hot coffee, they called the surface support vessel, a barge labeled *YFNB-12,* by telephone. Because the large helium content of the Sealab atmosphere distorted their voices, the message was routed through an "unscrambler." "We are doing fine," the aquanauts reported. "It is nice and comfortable down here. We could stay forever."

The divers checked the atmospheric controls to make certain that the breathing mixture in the capsule was maintained as required—80 percent helium, 16 percent nitrogen, and 4 percent oxygen. They also tested the communications systems, which included telephones, electrowriter, telegraphy, and television.

Then they commenced their first trip into the undersea world outside of the Sealab. Wearing specially modified scuba gear, they swam about the immediate area, observing the physical features and marine life of the ocean bottom and making brief sorties around the base of the Argus Island tower. Visibility was good; when looking vertically, the men could see clearly the hull of the support vessel on the ocean surface, 192 feet above them. Horizontally, their view extended 60 or 70 feet.

Before the men retired that evening, they were given extensive medical examinations [by Dr. Thompson and Hospital Corpsman Manning, along on the experiment]. Their condition was good.

Second day

The men awoke in good spirits, completed the morning's physiological and psychological examinations, then continued making general observations in the vicinity of the Sealab. By this time they were feeling quite at home in their new environment, even in the presence of many undersea creatures that shared it with them. Two large groupers were exceptionally friendly. They were easily distinguishable from others of the species, one of them having skin that looked like gray velvet (he was named Wally) and the other having a black fin and tail (he was called George).

The grouper, by the way, is a great gray sea bass. It can reach 400, 500, or even, off Australia, 800 to 1,200 pounds in weight. This big fish apparently enjoys keeping company with men on the bottom of the sea. At Assumption Reef, near Madagascar, Jacques-Yves Cousteau's divers encountered a grouper that nuzzled up to them, nibbled their swim fins, ate from their hands, and became so friendly it drove other fish away and got in the men's way. Jon Lindbergh and Robert Stenuit had groupers for company in their 49-hour, 432-foot dive in the Atlantic.

In the afternoon the Sealab team began a work program, the first objective of which was to imbed ultrasonic beacons in the ocean floor. The beacons were to be used by the swimmers as direction finders.

Late in the day the aquanauts were startled when, upon looking toward the ocean surface, they saw the entire fish community dive frantically toward the Sealab.

The reason for the stampede was soon evident: two 10-foot sharks were in pursuit. For about five minutes the sharks thoroughly upset the tranquillity of the area.

Third day

The day's assignments began with the drawing of blood samples and the recording of various physiological data. Later in the morning a trolley car, similar to a dumb-waiter, was put in operation between the surface and the undersea habitation to enable equipment and materials to be transferred rapidly between the two levels.

After lunch, the aquanauts took a one-hour nap. Aboard the support vessel on the ocean surface, Captain George F. Bond, medical officer in charge and originator of Project Sealab, observed the aquanauts' condition closely. He noted on this occasion, as he had on others during the past two days, that the divers were drowsier, particularly after eating, than they would have been at sea level. They also displayed, unknowingly, some lack of willingness to do physical work. Captain Bond commented, "They move slower than normal and do not like to be rushed. It seems as if they are making every effort to conserve their energy."

After their siesta, the aquanauts continued working "outdoors." They returned to their "home" at about 4:00 P.M., recorded their body temperatures, and took hot showers. They had an early evening meal, rested for an hour, then underwent more psychological and physiological testing.

They retired at about 9:00 P.M.

Fourth day

On their morning and afternoon swims, the aquanauts installed a current meter on the ocean floor, accomplishing the task in about 30 minutes, and assisted photographer-divers sent down from the surface in making a pictorial record of the Sealab operation.

In the evening, they took motion pictures of their activities in Sealab. Before retiring at 11:00 P.M., they engaged in long technical discussions with project officers on the surface support vessel.

The temperature within Sealab was now being maintained at 86 degrees Fahrenheit. This relatively high heat level was required because helium, the main ingredient of the breathing mixture supplied to the aquanauts, transfers heat at a rate approximately seven times that of air. [Maintenance of body heat is therefore a real problem.] Laboratory tests made before the Sealab project was undertaken had indicated that the temperature might have to be raised to 91 degrees Fahrenheit for human comfort. Thus six electric heaters had been installed in the small compartment. However, at no time had it been necessary to operate the heaters at full capacity.

Fifth day

All conditions were normal when the aquanauts awoke at 9:00 A.M. . . . .

After the physiological and psychological examinations were completed, Aquanaut Barth went out to feed the fish. By now he had so completely won the confidence of the groupers that they not only ate out of his hand, but on a few occasions tried to make off with his thumb, mistaking it for part of the meal. Barth carried the undersea television camera along so that personnel on the *YFNB-12* could watch the show on their television monitor. Kinescope recordings were made of the entire process, which lasted 75 minutes.

Later in the day, the aquanauts implanted devices on the ocean floor to measure underwater visibility.

In the evening, they rigged large spotlights around and above the Sealab to illuminate their habitat for the nighttime photography.

The physical condition of the men remained good.

Sixth day

When the aquanauts awoke this morning, they had been living on the ocean bottom for 144 hours.

During an early morning conversation with the surface vessel, Lieutenant Thompson told of trying to catch a trumpet fish. "Apparently," he said, "the trumpet fish will allow you to believe that you have captured him. Then, just as your grip tightens, he scoots away." Thompson told also of lowering a thermometer into the water to record the temperature outside of Sealab. As he did so, the groupers Wally and George, thinking food was being served, made several strikes at it.

At 10:30 A.M., the Sealab became an underwater chapel. Lieutenant Thompson thanked God for watching over them and giving them the friendship of the undersea creatures, and he asked that "the Lord take care of those who take care of us." The service was concluded with the singing of "Onward, Christian Soldiers," accompanied by Lieutenant Thompson on the harmonica.

Even though the sea was now heavier than it had been at any time since the experiment began, the day was both bright and peaceful in the underwater realm.

Seventh day

Today, Aquanaut Manning almost lost his life. The accident occurred during the visit to Sealab of *Star I,* an experimental one-man submarine built by the Electric Boat Division of General Dynamics Corporation. The dive was made to test the ability of the aquanauts to observe the craft's operation and to assist it in landing on a mockup of a submarine escape hatch.

Manning's job was to photograph the event. He had taken about 15 feet of film on a 50-foot roll, when he suddenly began feeling light-headed. Realizing that his scuba gear was not functioning properly (apparently his gas supply had been cut off, causing him to breathe his own exhalation), he commenced swimming back to the capsule. He had reached the entrance tube and had just begun to climb up it when he lost consciousness.

At that moment, Anderson, who was standing watch inside the capsule, heard an unusual sound. Apparently Manning's scuba gear struck the tube wall as he fell unconscious. Upon climbing down the tube to investigate, Anderson saw Manning's limp body drifting away. Quickly, he pulled him into the Sealab, removed his mask, and restored his normal breathing. Within five minutes he had revived completely, and after careful examination was found to be fit to continue the experiment. Fortunately, the only enduring physical effect of the experience was a reddening of his eyes.

At 5:35 P.M., the Navy's four-man aquanaut team marked its first week of residence in the Sealab—the longest period of time man had remained submerged, at this depth, under similar conditions. The men remained cheerful and content in their surroundings.

Eighth day

This morning the aquanauts completed a battery of medical tests to determine their condition after living for one week under the intense pressure of the 192-foot-depth level. To all indications, their health and spirits were excellent.

They now began conducting a series of shark experiments. The purpose of the investigation, which was conducted in cooperation with the University of Miami, was to determine the effects of sounds and colored lights on shark behavior. The aquanauts made extensive journeys outside of Sealab to install acoustic devices and electric lights for the experiment. The underwater television camera was positioned so that any shark coming into the area could be observed in complete safety. The men were to watch the action through the portholes in Sealab and from the heavily screened-in area under the habitat called the "back porch." [Sealab was supported six feet above the sea floor by struts that ended in pontoons resting on the floor; there was plenty of head room beneath Sealab for this screened-in area.]

Late in the afternoon a shortwave radio was installed in the Sealab, and a marine-band linkage was established through Washington, D.C., enabling the aquanauts to converse with people all over the United States. The first contact was made with a ham radio operator in Savannah, Georgia. The gentleman in Savannah found it difficult to believe that the transmission he was receiving came from a station 192 feet beneath the surface of the ocean.

The shark-attraction system was turned on in the evening for several hours, but no sharks appeared.

Ninth day

Late this morning, the aquanauts conversed by radio with Rear Admiral John K. Leydon, Chief of Naval Research, in Washington, D.C. Rear Admiral Leydon congratulated the aquanauts for the progress they had made thus far, and he wished them well during the remainder of their underwater sojourn.

Because the forecast for the next 24 hours called for bad weather at the Argus Island site (a storm was blowing up), Lieutenant Commander Roy E. Lanphear of the Office of Naval Research, Sealab's operational commander, decided to bring the aquanauts back to the surface. At 6:00 P.M., therefore, the topside cranes began hoisting the capsule toward the surface. The slow process of decompression, which could take as long as 96 hours, was carried out under the watchful eyes of Captain Bond. All systems in the Sealab continued to function perfectly.

Tenth day

Decompression continued on schedule under the close scrutiny of Sealab officers aboard the *YFNB-12*. The officers monitored the upward journey by means of television cameras located both inside and outside the capsule.

During the day, his Excellency, the Governor of Bermuda, Lord Martonmere, visited Argus Island to observe the operations underway in support of the project. The Governor was accompanied by the American Consul General, Mr. George W. Renchard; the Commanding Officer of the U.S. Naval Station, Bermuda, Captain Roy S. Belcher, U.S. Navy; and the Commanding Officer of the U.S. Air Force Base, Colonel Oren Poage.

By midnight, Sealab had been raised to the 100-foot level. At this point, with 18-foot swells running topside, surge effects on Sealab were so severe that further rise was hazardous; a prolonged "hold" was ordered. Through the night, in worsening weather, the capsule was inched toward the surface.

Eleventh day

At 7:32 A.M., the aquanauts left the Sealab at the 81-foot level and entered a submersible decompression chamber [suspended from the *YFNB-12*]. At 2:40 P.M., the chamber was raised onto the cargo deck of the Argus Island tower. The aquanauts were in excellent condition, and their spirits remained high.

Early the next morning, the hatch of the submersible decompression chamber was opened, and the four Navy aquanauts stepped into the sunshine of their natural environment. After brief discussions, they were flown to the U.S. Air Force Base Hospital at Bermuda for a medical debriefing. All tests indicated that the men were in good health.

Thus ended the log of the Sealab aquanauts, and thus ended their stay underwater. They had not been able to do some of the tasks originally planned: pouring concrete, drilling into the lava of the seamount upon which Argus Island is located, and mapping the ocean floor.

Before the Navy put its men into Sealab I, five years of experiments had been made which indicated that men could live on the sea floor unharmed. Tests on both animals and men in a pressure chamber (a tank on dry land containing air or gas under pressure) showed that men could live safely and perform useful functions for long periods of time under pressures up to 100 pounds per square inch. Chief Quartermaster Barth and Chief Hospital Corpsman Manning, who were Sealab dwellers on the sea bottom, lived for 12 days in a pressurized tank at the Naval Medical Research Laboratory, New London, Connecticut, breathing an artificial atmosphere, largely helium. With them during their stay in the dry-land tank was Lieutenant John Bull, a doctor from the nuclear-powered fleet ballistic missile submarine *Abraham Lincoln.*

The pressurized tank, or climate-altitude chamber, at New London is unique: It can duplicate pressures found from an ocean depth of 250 feet to an altitude of 200,000 feet, a wide range of atmospheres, and has good control over temperature, humidity, and sound levels.

The 9-foot-square climate-altitude chamber is 7 feet in height. The chamber is one of man's new tools for research on conditions for living and working on the sea bottom. It was installed at the Medical Research Laboratory as recently as July 1963.

After living in the chamber 12 days, Barth and Manning underwent 27 hours of decompression before they stepped out of the chamber. They had even gained weight.

The Navy's helium-oxygen mixture for breathing was proved out on a series of tests made on white rats, guinea pigs, squirrel monkeys, and goats before it was tried on man. Similarly, the animals were exposed to two weeks of seven atmospheres of pressure before the men entered the climate-altitude chamber. The animals showed no signs of deterioration.

In a later experiment, three Navy chief petty officers lived in a two-section chamber, breathing an artificial atmosphere composed largely of helium. One section of the chamber was wet; the men, still under pressure of a depth of about 100 feet of seawater, could walk into a cylindrical wet room, 10 feet in diameter and 18 feet deep, where they could do special energy-consuming work, such as they might do on the sea floor.

From Sealab I, the Navy passed in late summer 1965 to Sealab II. This was, the authoritative magazine *Sea Frontiers* commented, "the most extensive test yet of man's ability to live and work in the ocean depths." From August to October, on the south rim of the sea-canyon off La Jolla and San Diego, California, where the Cousteau-Westinghouse diving saucer had explored, the Navy kept three teams of 10 men each for 15 days at a depth of 205 feet. Astronaut and Aquanaut M. Scott Carpenter, a Navy commander and the second U.S. spaceman after John Glenn to be placed in orbit, stayed down for 30 days, a world's record at this depth. Carpenter's space trip took place on May 24, 1962; he made three orbits of the earth in a one-man Mercury spacecraft. He is the only man in the world to be both an astronaut and an aquanaut. In addition, the Navy doctor-aquanaut Lt. Robert Sonnenburg served on two teams, thus being exposed to 30 days at depth, but undergoing two decompression periods as well.

Sealab II was located 4,000 feet off the shore of the campus of the Scripps Institution of Oceanography of the University of California, San Diego.

"Sealab II," the Navy says, "is a non-propelled, seagoing craft, much like a submarine, which can be lowered into the ocean depths and emplaced on the ocean floor. It will serve as an artificial habitat wherein ten aquanauts can live for prolonged periods in an artificial atmosphere."

Sealab II was bigger than Sealab I: It was 57 feet long, 12 feet in diameter, and stood on a thick steel frame. Its one-inch-thick walls would withstand 188 pounds of pressure per square inch. The interior of Sealab II was kept at a temperature of 80-to-90 degrees Fahrenheit and a humidity of 60 percent, comfortable in the high-helium atmosphere and warm against the 47- to 50-degree water outside.

Work was provided for the men of Sealab II. A junked Navy fighter aircraft was sunk so the men might use a new buoyant plastic foaming technique to float it to the surface. The attempt succeeded. A piece of steel hull simulating a submarine hull was sunk so the divers could repair it with a rivet gun and attach experimental rubber flotation bags to see if they could float it to the surface. They also performed tasks ordinarily performed in ore mining (such as picking up mineral samples with a suction gun) and in assembling, maintaining, and repairing an undersea "weather station." They studied the geology of the ocean bottom, especially sediment; they measured currents; and the marine biologists among them assembled a 10-foot-square fish cage on the ocean floor to provide an aquarium beneath the sea. They performed a series of experiments, including the taking of internal gas samples from fish swim-bladders (as in the gas bubbles of fish that reflect sound and may cause the mysterious deep scattering layer). Bioluminescence and biofluorescence of marine life were studied and plankton sampled. They saw sea lions eat squid, squid eat fish, and fish swallow small anchovies. Sometimes a seal would gobble a fish as the fish gulped an anchovy.

The divers, including Spaceman Carpenter, were stung right through their rubber suits by moderately poisonous scorpion fish. "Excursion dives" were performed by all aquanauts, extending over the edge of the nearby Scripps Canyon to an ultimate depth of 300 feet.

The Sealab II workers were assisted by a new helper trained by Dr. Sam H. Ridgway, a veterinary medicine graduate of Texas A. & M.: Tuffy. Tuffy, a 7-foot-long, 270-pound porpoise, carried messages in a special harness. He hauled a letter to Mrs. John

Reaves, the wife of an aquanaut, from bottom to surface. He was trained to carry lifelines to any of the aquanauts who might get lost in nearby deep, murky waters. He did. "The porpoise," says the Navy, "responded instantly and unerringly to acoustic signals given by divers stationed . . . beyond his range of sight." And he served as a lifeguard. If sharks appeared, Tuffy was released from his pen on the surface to see if he would chase them away. Tuffy got his name because of his many honorable scars, earned skirmishing with sharks. "In tanks ashore," says Dr. Ridgway, a research veterinarian, "we have seen porpoises attack sharks in captivity by butting them." After Sealab II, Tuffy located a missile-launch cradle to which a buzzer had been attached, and led Navy frogmen to it. The cradle, in 50 feet of water, was recovered. Previous attempts to recover the launch cradles had failed.

At one time a doctor, Samuel Bellet, sat in his office at Philadelphia General Hospital—a continent away from Sealab II—and watched for the recorded heartbeat of one of the Sealab II divers on the bottom of the sea. The heartbeat was picked up by a sonar-like process from the diver, sent through the water to Sealab II, sent by wire to the barge on the surface, and telephoned long-distance across the nation to Dr. Bellet's office. Unfortunately, a minor relay failure at the end of the line lost the signal, but the experiment was nevertheless rated a success.

Scott Carpenter thought man's ability to adjust helped the divers. "When we first went out of Sealab II," he said, "we would swim 25 or 30 minutes [in that 47- to 50-degree water], then shiver so badly it was unbelievable. But within two weeks we were staying out for an hour or more."

From the bottom of the sea in Sealab II, Carpenter talked with Astronauts L. Gordon Cooper, Jr., and Charles Conrad as they orbited in Gemini V.

Sealab II, the Navy said, participated in "the longest and most ambitious deep-diving experiment ever conducted." To the aquanauts afterward, Secretary of the Navy Paul H. Nitze said, "You have proved that men can live and do useful work under the sea. Your accomplishments during the past 45 days have set one of the cornerstones for our future exploitation of the continental shelf."

As for Tuffy, the porpoise, the Navy concluded that he had showed the porpoise "may have earned a place beside man in the exploration and exploitation of the undersea world." A second porpoise, Buzz Buzz, today is being trained to assist Tuffy.

Captain Jacques-Yves Cousteau, in the Mediterranean off Monaco, meanwhile was also making an undersea-living experiment, with Conshelf III. He kept 6 French oceanauts 3 weeks in an undersea station in the Mediterranean 325 feet deep—the deepest prolonged submersion yet. The French divers were given daily jobs under André Laban, one of the men who had piloted the diving saucer off the U.S. west coast. They worked on a simulated undersea oil well 370 feet down for five hours at a time ("tough but acceptable"). They made short trips as far as 390 feet down. "The six French oceanauts," the National Geographic Society, which has supported Captain Cousteau's projects, reports, "breathed a mixture of helium and oxygen at 11 atmospheres of pressure. Nitrogen had to be removed to prevent toxic effects under high pressure. The men were quartered in a spherical, two-story house put under this pressure for three days before it was lowered to the sea floor. They had to remain inside for several days after surfacing so that they could be slowly decompressed. In all, they spent a month under pressure."

Cousteau's undersea living experiments and the long-term program of the U.S. Navy have shown that men can adjust physically and mentally to work at the depths over the continental shelf. Cousteau's Conshelf III, said Dr. Melville Bell Grosvenor, president of the National Geographic Society, vastly increased the area of the world accessible to human exploration.

"Within five years, if the program continues as it has," Captain

George Bond of the Navy Medical Corps says, "I feel we will be doing useful work at 800-foot depths with crews of as many as 300 men living underwater for long periods of time."

William Tolbert, a diver on Sealab II, who is already a volunteer for Sealab III (a 450-foot-deep underwater home to be operated by the Navy), gave to a reporter for *The National Observer* an additional thought: "For all of us," he said, "it was the best time we've ever had, made us feel we weren't working hard enough, that it shouldn't be this much fun."

CHAPTER
19

"Man Will Adapt
to Undersea"

"IT IS no great chore for an experienced diver to work on deeply submerged equipment in the dead of night without the aid of lighting. It is hard to conceive of a device which could readily replace this tremendous advantage afforded the diver."

This comes from K. G. Young, Jr., an ocean engineer for Reading and Bates Offshore Drilling Company in Tulsa, Oklahoma. A man, he says, has something no robot yet can duplicate: a sense of touch.

"The diver's world," says Mr. Young, "is often a murky, visually tenuous place in which to work. His one infallible contact with the environment is his sense of touch."

So Mr. Young and Reading and Bates plan to put men on the sea floor and keep them there. To do this, they plan the most versatile undersea vehicle yet. Reading and Bates calls it the General Purpose Submersible, or GPS. The GPS is like a self-propelled, deeper-diving Sealab II.

The GPS will take a party of men from the surface to the bottom (as will either a deep-diving submarine or diving bell). Once on the bottom, it will provide living quarters that keep the men in good shape (as did the big metal shelters of Sealabs I and II). It will allow the men to go out onto the ocean floor and work there (as a diving bell does, and the Sealabs did, though only a few submarines can).

Because of his sense of touch—and because he is an eyewitness —a man can do lots of jobs, especially the unexpected ones, more easily than an unmanned mechanical device, Mr. Young points out. Human divers can do the chores that arise on the spur of the moment: underwater welding, repairing, and picking up dropped tools. It is often more convenient for divers to make hose connections that were designed to be made by robots. "The diver," says Mr. Young, "is the offshore 'plumber,' construction worker, surveyor, photographer, and 'Mark I eyeball-computer-manipulator combination.' "

There is still another reason to put man on the sea floor: he adapts. "In a great many respects," Mr. Young comments, "the sea environment is more hostile than land. But the fact is, and it is man's unique advantage, that he is the 'great adapter.' Man has demonstrated the capability to acclimate himself to all known terrestrial environments which require his presence—including the near-earth space."

Basically the General Purpose Submersible will consist of three long, cylindrical hulls. One hull, fatter than the others, will be in between and slightly above the other two.

The fat center hull will provide living quarters for the men, who will dive in and work out of the GPS. It will provide storage for their equipment. It will provide fresh water and bathrooms. A kitchen and food storage will be similar to those aboard the Polaris submarines.

The breathing gas in the central hull, an oxygen-helium mixture, will be kept at a pressure equivalent to that of the depth at which the General Purpose Submersible is located. This will prevent the seawater from entering. Men will leave the central hull to go out into the sea to work through a diving port that has direct access to the sea.

When they return from the sea, as in Sealab II, the men will find dryness and warmth inside the central hull. Hot showers will restore their body heat.

The two slimmer, cigar-shaped hulls, beneath and to each side of the central hull, provide the General Purpose Submersible with her ballast, trim tanks, engine rooms, and fuel and water storage. They also help support the central cylinder when the GPS is on the bottom. Men in the GPS will be able to live satisfactorily on the sea floor for several weeks.

The first GPS will be for use on the continental shelf, up to a depth of around 600 feet. This means the men in the GPS can work on underwater oil wells. Mr. Young thinks that most such work will be on the sea bottom in the future, instead of on offshore platforms. "The advantage of being underwater," he says, "is that you eliminate problems: The tides, currents, weather, and traffic of ships and small boats are things you do not have to worry about." Other jobs for GPS would be underwater construction, sewer outfalls, aquaculture (raising fish as farm crops), salvage of ships, and recovery of minerals.

When the General Purpose Submersible is ready to carry her men to the bottom, she will descend with the help of inflatable buoyancy floats, an important difference between GPS and a submarine. The floats, sort of underwater balloons, will be attached by lines to the GPS and surround her and slow up her descent.

When the GPS has reached the bottom, the floats will be hauled aboard, deflated, and stored in lockers.

The GPS, like a bathyscaphe, will be propelled for a short distance underwater by a battery-powered motor, but she will not be as capable of extensive underwater travel as a deep-diving submarine.

When ready to ascend, she will deploy her inflatable buoyancy floats, and start upward. Her central hull, the men's living quarters, can be used as a decompression chamber. On the surface she will be driven by conventional diesel marine engines.

The men from the General Purpose Submersible will be able to do everything around an undersea oil well—all types of maintenance and repair—except drill the well itself.

Reading and Bates's plans for the next step, once the General Purpose Submersible is built, include a submersible whose men will actually drill oil wells. It will be known as Subrig.

Subrig will be oddly shaped for a ship: it will look like a pyramid. What Reading and Bates plan to do is to take the derrick usually seen over an offshore oil platform, plus the platform (or deck) under the derrick where the men live, and enclose the whole business in a watertight hull, like the hulls of the General Purpose Submersible or the hull of a submarine. The Subrig will be pressurized with oxygen-helium, like the GPS center hull.

Subrig will be lowered to the sea floor, using inflatable buoyancy floats similar to those of the GPS. Buoys on the surface will mark Subrig's position and provide communications to the surface or to shore. A snorkel outlet will bring down air to the diesel engines that will operate the well's draw works.

Subrig will be able to stay down in one place for several months, and her crew would be able to drill several wells without moving. Personnel would be rotated to and from her by means of a submersible elevator, or diving bell.

Planned for water 30 to 600 feet deep, Reading and Bates expects Subrig to be in business by the 1970's.

Reading and Bates's elevator, or diving bell, now in use, carries seven men to the bottom. Its name is the Submersible Work Chamber.

And that is what it is: A steel elevator that is used also, on the return trip, to decompress divers. A returning diver enters it on the sea floor. It hoists him back up onto the deck of a barge on the surface. He remains inside as long as necessary to decompress. Or he may transfer to a decompression chamber on deck to compress. He does not have to be kept in the water for an extended period, as was formerly the case.

On the sea floor, the Submersible Work Chamber remains near its working divers. It provides them with a seabed source of tools and breathing gas.

The SWC also can be lowered only part way to the bottom to provide a scaffolding for work between the surface and the sea floor.

The SWC will be used in installing and maintaining offshore oil equipment, and as a research tool by oceanographers and other explorers of the sea.

Mr. Young foresees a future in which man will "reap the ocean's harvest." Man has today, Mr. Young says, the technological knowledge he needs. He feels that Reading and Bates's machines are an example of this technology. But more will be needed: man himself.

"We feel certain," he says, "that man will adapt to the deep undersea environment and that the most economical means of working in deep water will be a combination of man and machine at the work site."

PART VI / *Into the Utmost Depths*

What the Deepest
Trawl Haul Caught

THE SUSPENSE built up. "Everybody on board who could leave his job," said Anton F. Bruun, "gathered round."

The trawl was coming up from the far bottom of the sea, from the floor of the Philippine Trench, over six miles down, the third- or fourth-deepest place in all the oceans. The Philippine Trench had never been trawled before. The trawl about to reach the surface was coming up from the deepest trawl any men ever had made.

Would it contain anything?

For the men aboard the *Galathea* that morning—it was a little before dawn on July 22, 1951—the biggest question was, as for a hundred years it had been for marine biologists, "Is there life at the deepest bottom of the sea? Can animals possibly exist over six miles down? If so, have we ever seen such animals? What are they like?"

The *Galathea* was an oceanographic research ship from Denmark. Chief of the expedition was Anton F. Bruun, the No. 1 Danish sea scientist and one of the top sea scientists in Europe and the world. The *Galathea,* a former British and New Zealand sloop of 1,600 tons, was 266 feet long, 34 feet wide, 11 feet in draft. Built at Devonport, England, in 1934, she was driven by two 1,000-horsepower steam turbines, had two oil-fired burners, and two three-blade propellers.

On October 15, 1950, she had set out for a round-the-world cruise with the objective of fishing the greatest depths of the sea.

The deepest places of all in the ocean are the great trenches that cut far into the sea floor. There is one in the Atlantic, the Puerto Rico Trench north of Puerto Rico. There are seven in the Pacific: the Kermadec, the Kurile-Kamchatka, the Marianas, the Japan, the Aleutian, the Tonga, and the Philippine east of Mindanao, which the *Galathea* was plumbing. No other ocean has comparable gashes in its floor. Roger Revelle and Robert Fisher of Scripps described a typical Pacific trench as so deep that seven Grand Canyons could be piled on top of each other in it, and so long that it would run from New York City to Kansas City. Dr. Fisher makes maps of the deep parts of the trenches. The trenches are perhaps the most striking feature of the earth's surface. Elongated and narrow, they are more than twice the average depth of the oceans. They vary from 5 to 7 miles in depth: from 27,510 feet for the Puerto Rico Trench to 36,200 feet for the Marianas Trench and 37,782 feet for the Cook Deep east of the Philippines, discovered only in 1962. Exactly how the great trenches were formed is one of the unsolved mysteries of the sea. They occur near mountain ranges or arcs of islands, however, and are associated with mountain building, active volcanoes, and earthquakes. Perhaps, while mountain ranges rise nearby, the crust of the earth dips in long, narrow furrows in a kind of opposing force.

Only two ships had attempted trawls in trenches before *Galathea,* and the depths of their trawls were not comparable with hers. Both were in 1948: The *Albatross,* a Swedish ship, had trawled 26,000 feet down on the east slope of the Puerto Rico Trench. The Soviet research ship *Vitiaz* made a single haul at 26,565 feet in the Kurile-Kamchatka Trench.

In the Philippine Trench, *Galathea*'s trawl had been dropped almost two miles farther down. The trawl was at the end of 7½ miles of a special wire; tapered wire, to reduce weight when it was all paid out. It was 22 millimeters thick at the end fastened to the winch, 9 millimeters thick at the trawl end. The wire's breaking point was 34 tons at its thickest section, 7 tons at its thinnest.

To help point out a likely spot to trawl, *Galathea* was equipped with a specially designed echo sounder by Kelvin-Hughes. The sound impulse this sounder sent forth was a whistling tone of 10,000 oscillations per second. The depths measured by the echo sounder were written automatically on paper. Over the Philippine Trench, the sounder showed this great gash in the sea floor as perhaps the largest in the world at such a depth: The trench stretches for an unbroken distance of 540 nautical miles below more than 4.64 miles of water. The greatest depth the echo sounder found in the trench was 33,678 feet, or 6.3 miles. Another ship, the *Cape Johnson,* had found 34,439 feet only 3½ nautical miles to the north.

The echo sounder located a likely—that is, a very deep—place for the *Galathea*'s first Philippine Trench trawl.

The trawl was lowered. The winch slowly paid out the wire. Toward dawn on July 22, 1951, the trawl was hauled up. As it approached the surface, all hands who could be spared gathered around to watch. The scene was described by Anton Bruun:

> There, deep down in the clear water, was the faint outline of the large triangular bag of the sledge-trawl. It was pitch-black night, but the quarter-deck lay bathed in the beams of our spotlights. Standing by the trawl gallows, watching the trawl breaking surface, was the fishmaster, his arms waving in a slow circle.
>
> At the winch all eyes were intently following the motions of his arms, as they slowed down and then came to a stop, the hand raised as a signal to stop hauling in. It all went with a fine rhythm of experienced teamwork, but the occasion was a special one: it was the first time that the indicator had stood at zero after reaching 12,163 meters, the full length of our wire.

Would there be anything in the trawl? The scientists, officers, and men aboard the *Galathea* steeled themselves for disappointment. "We comforted ourselves with the thought that it was the first attempt with the full length of our new wire, that everything had gone like clockwork all night, that the wire was safely home and we should be able to make a fresh attempt; yes, it was a relief to know that we should be able to try again, even in the Philippine Trench."

Soon there appeared to be at least some reason for optimism. "There's clay on the frame!" somebody cried. "It's been on the bottom!" And then: "There are stones in the bag!"

Soon nervous fingers were loosening the trawl.

> We hardly noticed the red prawns, luminescent euphausiids, or black fishes; we all knew these to be pelagic animals, caught on the way up through the free water masses. But there, on a rather large stone, were some small whitish growths—sea anemones! Even if no more animals had been found, this would still be the outstanding haul of the expedition. It was proof that higher animals can live deeper than 10,000 meters. Is it surprising that all were overjoyed?

But there was more to come.

> And that pleasure became excitement when out of the grayish clay with gravel and stones we picked altogether 25 sea anemones, about 75 sea cucumbers, five bivalves, one amphipod, and one bristle-worm. It was an unexpectedly rich variety of bottom-dwelling animals.
>
> That the haul had been made on the bottom was obvious, and fortunately we had all the proofs that it was at 10,190 meters. We had carefully navigated according to the configuration of the bottom laboriously pieced together from our echo sounding on many days before; on the bridge they had calculated the driftage due to current with such accuracy that our depth through-

out had never been less than 10,190 meters; wind and
sea had been very slight from the north, almost head on,
as favorable as they could possibly be. Forgotten was the
long night vigil; our success had to be followed up,
everything repeated if possible. . . .

Everything was not repeated.

The *Galathea* dropped her trawl five more times in the Philippine Trench. She caught a few more animals on some of her tries,
but bottom conditions, currents, waves, and winds kept all her
further efforts from being as successful as her first. She did pick up
more sea anemones, sea cucumbers, another bristle-worm, the remains of five greenish little echiuroid worms, another bivalve, and
some small crustaceans (isopods).

"We had found a whole little animal community," Bruun said.
"All the large groups of invertebrates were represented—polyps,
worms, echinoderms, mollusks, and crustaceans. The known depth
limit of life had been pushed some 2.5 kilometers [1.35 miles]
lower down."

Galathea's trawl had proved there was life all the way to the
deepest bottom of the sea, over six miles down.

A few days earlier, the *Galathea* had received an indication of
what to expect. On July 15 she had hauled up a sample of mud
from Station No. 413, in the Philippine Trench. Claude E. ZoBell,
professor of microbiology at the Scripps Institution, was anxious to
examine the muck for bacteria. "The average diameter of bacteria,"
Professor ZoBell has written, "is near one micron [a micron is one
ten-thousandth of a centimeter]. In spite of their small size, bacteria
are so numerous that they may constitute an appreciable part of the
volume or total weight of living organisms in the sea." Bacteria in
the mud would be a clue that life was possible there.

A 1,000-power microscope showed bacteria in the mud. When
so magnified, some appeared to be about the size of a period on
this page; others resembled commas or rods. Were they alive?
Dead? Fossils? Professor ZoBell put samples of the mud, together

with nutrients he hoped would be suitable for such bacteria, plus seawater, peptone, and yeast extract in glass tubes. All this went into a refrigerator where the pressure was stepped up to 1,000 atmospheres; in other words, everything was made as much like home as possible for the bacteria from the bottom of the Philippine Trench.

Several days later the bacteria were examined again. They had grown and had reproduced in great numbers; they had affected the chemical composition of the medium in which they had been placed. These were the first living things ever discovered at such a great depth, and the first proof of the growth and activity of organisms at a pressure as high as that of the Philippine Trench. The deep-sea bacteria, it has been learned, will not grow and reproduce unless they are under a pressure equal to that of the deep sea; hence they have been named pressure-loving bacteria. Bringing up the bacteria indicated to Anton Bruun, the *Galathea* expedition leader, that there probably would indeed be other animal life in the Philippine Trench—as the world's deepest trawl proved there was.

Before and since the *Galathea*'s feat, sea scientists have been able to trawl at depths only rarely (and only the *Albatross* and *Vitiaz* in 1948 had been able to reach into the trenches at all). The first two ships to trawl deep waters, a century ago, belonged to the British Navy. They were *Porcupine* and *Lightning*. They were directed by Dr. W. B. Carpenter and Professor (later Sir) Wyville Thomson. During 1868–70, they made 200 dredge hauls north and west of the British Isles. They brought up a wealth of life. Thomson published a book about it in 1873, entitled *The Depths of the Sea*. It was one of the first books to acquaint any considerable public with oceanography. The discoveries of the *Porcupine* and *Lightning,* Thomson's book, and the need for more information about the depths of the sea when some of the Atlantic telegraph cables were being laid, led the British Government in December 1872 to dispatch H.M.S. *Challenger,* a wooden sail-and-steam corvette, on a 3½-year expedition through all the world's seas. Her captain was George Nares. Wyville Thomson was director. The *Challenger* crossed and recrossed the Atlantic. She was the first steamship to cross the Antarctic Circle, and she made the first scientific exploration of the Pacific, trawling round the world before either steam trawls or wire rope had been invented. She could not, of course, trawl nearly so deep as *Galathea,* but she did bring back information on the chemistry of the sea, its physics, its depths, its bottom conditions, its temperature and composition, its currents, its sediments and—most of all—the life in the sea. *Challenger*'s scientists thought of oceanography as the study "of the seas and all that in them is"—still probably the best definition today. Oceanography, as H. V. R. Palmer, Jr., a retired Navy captain, commented to me at Woods Hole, is not a science but a field: a field of many sciences applied to the sea. *Challenger*'s reports filled 50 volumes and weighed a quarter of a ton. The 50 volumes remain a classic of oceanography; they are the foundation of today's sea science and of the exploration of the depths. John Murray, the famous publisher, was one of her biologists and the editor of her reports. They are so significant that they are being republished in the United States by the Johnson Reprint Corporation of New York City, at $3,850 a set.

Prince Albert of Monaco trawled successfully from his *Princesse Alice II* in 1901 at a new record depth: just under 20,000 feet. Albert made a series of oceanographic cruises and founded the world-famous Oceanographic Museum in Monaco.

A round-the-world expedition to trawl at some depth was that of the Carlsberg Foundation and the Danish ship *Dana II* in 1928–30. The Danish expedition was led by Johannes Schmidt, Denmark's great sea scientist. Schmidt made his name famous by finding the breeding places of fresh-water European eels. Crossing the Atlantic in ship after ship, he lowered nets and captured specimens of eel larvae. As he sailed west, they became smaller and smaller. He found the transparent, glassy, leaf-shaped larvae at their smallest beneath the Sargasso Sea, in the heart of the Atlantic Ocean.

Before Schmidt the birthplace of the European eels had not been known. Schmidt placed it at about 1,200 feet deep. Further study showed the American eel spawned nearby in the Sargasso Sea, a little nearer the American coast. It takes about three years for an eel larva to reach Europe via the Gulf Stream; it has changed into a small wriggly eel in the meantime. It takes about a year for the American eel to reach an American river. Neither Schmidt nor anyone since has completed the story on eels. And no one has found an adult eel en route to the Sargasso Sea, nor has anyone ever found eel eggs.

Anton Bruun was along with Johannes Schmidt aboard the *Dana II* in 1930; on that expedition one morning he had an experience that shaped his life. It was an adventure with an eel larva, a huge one. He watched the trawl come aboard after it had sampled life on the sea floor at a point in the Atlantic to the west of South Africa. Most of the fish and animals he recognized. One, however, startled him. It was transparent, glassy, leaf-shaped, like any other eel larva, but with a difference: the European and American larvae that Johannes Schmidt and Anton Bruun had become familiar with were up to 3 inches in length. They grew into eels usually 2 or 3 feet long as adults; sometimes as much as 10 or 16 feet. But the larva in the trawl aboard the *Dana* was 6 feet long. It proved to be the larva of a great unknown eel. It could grow—if it grew at the same ratio as do known eel larvae—into a sea serpent 80, 100, or 180 feet long.

The *Dana*'s trawl was hauled up only a few miles from the position where Captain Peter M'Quhae and Midshipman Sartoris, aboard the British frigate *Daedalus* on August 6, 1848, had sighted an enormous eellike monster on the surface. The incident since has been referred to many times as one of the authentic sightings of the sea serpent. Captain M'Quhae described it as "an enormous serpent, with head and shoulders kept about four feet constantly above the surface of the sea, and as nearly as we could approximate . . . there was at the very least 60 feet of the animal (in sight on the surface). . . . It passed rapidly, but so close under our lee quarter, that had it been a man of my acquaintance I should have easily recognized his features with the naked eye; and it did not, either in approaching the ship or after it had passed our wake, deviate in the slightest degree from its course to the S.W., which it held on at the pace of from 12 to 15 miles per hour."

Bruun, who died December 13, 1961, spent much time during the rest of his life looking for the adult of his 6-foot-long eel larva —the sea serpent. He never found it. "If the monstrous larva exists," Bruun said, "the monstrous adults must exist, too—as terrifying as any sea serpent ever painted. . . . I am a man who rather believes in sea serpents."

Today the U.S. National Science Foundation operates an oceanographic research vessel named the *Anton Bruun.* She is the former Presidential yacht *Williamsburg.*

One day in Denmark in 1941, Bruun gave a lecture on the possibility of sea serpents truly existing, and said he had proof: that great eel larva. It may be seen today in the University Zoological Museum in Copenhagen.

A man named Hakon Mielche heard Bruun's speech, was intrigued by it, and persuaded Bruun to raise the money and set out on a round-the-world voyage to plumb the farthest depths to see what was there. The *Galathea* expedition that reached to the bottom of the Philippine Trench was the result. Elsewhere on her circumnavigation of the world, at other depths, all shallower, the *Galathea* also caught a host of unknown or little-known animals. "Before reaching Australia," P. L. Kramp reported, "we had found nearly 150 different species of medusae (jellyfish), 20 of them previously unknown."

Other specimens taken by *Galathea* were:

A white sea spider from over three miles down in the Sunda Deep, the deepest ever caught.

A lobster without eyes, from black depths two miles down.

Sea snails from the Sunda Deep, the deepest ever caught, breaking a record held by the Prince of Monaco.

Sea snakes that are cousins to the cobra, and very poisonous.

A fire-engine-red shrimp previously unknown.

A small black fish, shaped like a submarine.

Trachyrincus, a deep-dwelling fish, shaped like a sweet potato.

The smallest shark ever found, a 15-centimeter *Etmopterus,* caught in the Gulf of Panama.

A short, fat deep-sea eel—not slender or snakelike—the *Coloconger,* taken off Natal.

A hermit crab with a colony of corallike animals surrounding it; other hermit crabs overgrown by a reddish-violet sea anemone, off Madagascar.

A brotulid, *Bassogigas,* caught 3,300 feet deeper than any previously found fish, in the Sunda Deep.

A rose-colored, swimming (not bottom-dwelling) sea cucumber, caught repeatedly: between Africa and Ceylon, in the Bay of Bengal, in the Kermadec Trench, and in the Gulf of Panama.

Stylephorus, a silvery, ribbon-shaped fish that swims with its head up and its tail down. It has large eyes: "Its binoculars," said P. L. Kramp, "can be turned both upward and forward."

Vampyroteuthis infernalis, the "vampire squid of the infernal regions." Ten-armed, it is related to cephalopods extinct since Cretaceous times, and Grace Pickford, an American biologist, considers it one of the more exciting zoological discoveries of the twentieth century. The *Galathea* did not discover it, but obtained the longest specimen ever, 8½ inches, off Durban. Its velvety, blue-black body reaches 3 inches in diameter. *Vampyroteuthis* can tuck into pockets in its body its two longest, slender arms. It may well have, Buchsbaum and Milne, the zoologists, figure, the largest eyes in proportion to its body of any animal. A 6-inch specimen had a pair of eyes an inch across—as large as the eyes of many grown dogs. The eyes may see light far dimmer than a man can.

Neopilina, a previously uncaught missing link in the mollusk family (the snails, clams, and octopuses).

Fishing off Mexico near the end of her cruise, in 11,878 feet of water, *Galathea* brought up 10 live specimens of the little snail-like neopilina, supposedly extinct for 350 million years, or since long before the dinosaurs died out. *Galathea*'s largest neopilina was 1 inch long, 1¼ inches wide, and ½ inch high. Since then, the Russians have found another species. And Columbia University scientists, headed by J. Lamar Worzel (who directed the *Conrad* in the search for the *Thresher*) in 1958 brought up four neopilina. The creatures were caught in nets at a depth of more than three miles in the Milne-Edwards Trench 200 miles west of Lima, Peru. "In the sense that neopilina is a living animal which has changed very little from ancestors five hundred million years ago," said Dr. John Imbrie, associate professor of geology at Columbia, "neopilina is one of the two oldest living animal links to the past." The other, about as old, is *Lingula,* a shell-bearing animal living in shallow waters off Japan.

Twenty years before the *Galathea*'s cruise, the *Dana II,* which captured the great eel larva, had caught also the world's greatest collection of deep-sea angler fishes. *Galathea* added to the collection. As late as May 6, 1952, on one of her last trawls—in the Pacific off Central America—*Galathea* brought up a formidable, previously unknown angler fish, a giant of its kind—half a yard long. It was from a depth of 11,778 feet. It was black and had a broad head. "To my colleagues' and my own delight," said Bruun, "I had to admit I had seen nothing like it on the *Dana.*"

This angler fish lures other fish to eat by means of a large light organ inside its mouth. Suspended from the roof of the mouth, it is behind pointed, curved teeth. As the mouth gapes, the light attracts prey to swim in and be eaten. A tiny similar angler (8 centimeters long) had been taken by an American expedition in 1908, but nothing like *Galathea*'s giant. So a name was given it, *Galatheathauma axeli,* after the ship and the chairman of the expedition committee, Prince Axel of Denmark. This living mouse trap, Anton Bruun felt, is "unquestionably the strangest catch of the *Galathea* expedition, and altogether one of the oddest creatures in the teeming variety of the fish world but," he added, "we caught only one, right at the end of the cruise."

The fisherman who had dropped his trawl line deeper than anyone else, who had made known to science as many rare or completely new sea creatures as any man of modern times, still had one regret about the cruise of the *Galathea*. One job was unfinished. "No one," he said, "has caught the great sea serpent."

CHAPTER
21

Over Six Miles Down,
Men Look Around

IN THE BATHYSCAPHE *Trieste,* designed to reach the deepest sea floor, the two men were trying to do just that. For four solid hours, they had dropped, dropped, dropped. They passed 20,000 feet down. They passed 30,000 feet. They dropped deeper yet. They reached the depth where, they thought, the bottom should have been; yet they kept right on sinking down, down, down. Twenty-four hundred feet below where they had believed the bottom to be, the *Trieste*'s floodlight dimly illuminated a nether world where no man ever had been. A grayish-white surface appeared: the sea floor, at last. "The bottom appeared light and clear, a waste of snuff-colored ooze," Jacques Piccard said. "We were landing on a nice, flat bottom of firm diatomaceous ooze." There came a slight bump. The *Trieste,* Piccard, and Lieutenant Donald Walsh, U.S. Navy, had made it. They were well over six miles below the surface of the sea.

On that January 22, 1960, they had reached, 200 miles from Guam in the Pacific, the bottom of the Challenger Deep of the Marianas Trench. "Their verified depth," Dr. D. A. Wilson, head of undersea technology at the Navy Electronics Laboratory says, "was 35,800 feet down—the deepest known place in the oceans, and, of course, a world's record dive." The men spent 20 minutes on the bottom, then came up. The round trip had taken nine hours.

Piccard and Walsh went as far down in the sea as big jet passenger planes today go up in the air on long flights.

The *Trieste* churned up silt off the bottom. The silt settled back down. Then, with their own eyes, Piccard and Walsh saw the answer to a question that man had always wondered about, to which the *Galathea,* in 1951, had obtained the very first answer: Is there life in the deepest parts of the sea? "As we were settling this final fathom," said Piccard, "I saw a wonderful thing. Lying on the bottom just beneath us was some type of flatfish, resembling a sole, about 1 foot long and 6 inches across." It was, Piccard said, a true fish, a teleost. The *Galathea* had trawled up animals from the bottom—sea anemones, sea cucumbers, bristle-worms, etc.— but had failed to catch a fish on the bottom.

As Piccard and Walsh watched, the flatfish moved along the bottom, partly in ooze and partly in water, and slowly disappeared. The *Trieste*'s floodlight showed a smaller animal. "I saw a beautiful red shrimp," said Piccard. The *Galathea* had trawled up red shrimp. It was an inch long. "Here, in an instant," he continued, "was the answer that biologists had asked for centuries. Could life exist in the greatest depths of the ocean? It could!" By eyewitnessing the fish, Piccard and Walsh also shed light on another mystery of the depths: Are there currents in the deepest waters? There would have to be currents to bring in the oxygen that fish require to live.

The fish seen from the *Trieste* was the deepest fish man has ever seen. The deepest fish ever recorded earlier was one caught by the *Galathea* 23,400 feet down in the Sunda Deep in 1952. It was a brotulid, the fish with the big head and long tail that is known to dwell at and below 6,000 feet down, the depth reached by our new research submarine *Alvin. Galathea*'s brotulid was about 6½ inches long. It broke a record that had stood for around 50 years. The previous deepest-known fish had been one caught by Prince Albert of Monaco at a depth of 19,800 feet. Prince Albert's fish also was a brotulid: *Grimaldichthys profundissimus.* The name comes in part from the Prince's family name, Grimaldi.

"To have seen not just one but two live creatures at the bottom, especially with the equipment we had, was staggeringly lucky," Lieutenant Walsh said. "It was the equivalent of seeing a rare animal while sealed in a small steel ball on top of Mount Everest for 20 minutes in the middle of the night with no means of illumination but a flashlight fixed to the side of the sphere."

"No net, no sounding device, not even sonar gear can truly replace a diving boat!" Roger Revelle, the oceanographer, had enthused. The *Trieste* showed what he meant.

"The descent to the floor of the Marianas Trench marks not only a new diving record, but a successful advance into a completely new world," Cord-Christian Troebst wrote in *Conquest of the Sea*. "It means the entering of unknown territory on our planet, the penetration of a region which had appeared quite inaccessible a few years ago.

"With the *Trieste*'s dive in the Pacific, 47 times as deep as any submarine could go at that time, the conquest of the sea reached a decisive state."

Trieste had taken eyewitnesses over 6 miles down only 8½ years after the *Galathea* had obtained man's very first specimens of life at that level.

The trip to the Challenger Deep was dive No. 65 for the *Trieste*. It was what the Navy called Project Nekton, and was under the scientific direction of Dr. Andreas B. Rechnitzer. Dr. Rechnitzer himself had reached four miles down in a bathyscaphe. Of the many tests and scientific projects *Trieste* has carried out, this one, the Navy says, was "one of the most significant and spectacular."

Also significant and spectacular was *Trieste*'s part in the search off Boston, Massachusetts, in 1963 for the sunken U.S. nuclear submarine *Thresher* (see photographs).

"The bathyscaphe (deep boat)," the U.S. Navy Electronics Laboratory (NEL) says, "was conceived, designed, and constructed by Professor Auguste Piccard of Switzerland, and NEL's *Trieste* was the second one built. It was launched near Naples, Italy, in

1953. It reached two miles down off Italy in 1953 (at that time the world's record dive for a manned submersible) and it carried two passengers as it did so: Auguste Piccard, who had become famous as the first balloonist to soar into the stratosphere (in a balloon of his own design), and his son, Jacques.

"In 1957, the U.S. Office of Naval Research, through the efforts of Dr. Robert S. Dietz, formerly of NEL, contracted with Professor Piccard for a series of dives to evaluate the craft." Dr. Dietz was the first American to make a dive in *Trieste*. With Jacques Piccard, Dr. Dietz later wrote *Seven Miles Down,* an account of the dive into the Challenger Deep. This is the same Dr. Dietz who was along on the U.S. Coast and Geodetic Survey trip to the Indian Ocean, and who described the gigantic mud slides found to occur in that ocean (Chapter 9).

The dives in 1957 demonstrated the *Trieste*'s value. She was bought by the U.S. Navy. Jacques Piccard was employed to indoctrinate naval personnel in the operation and maintenance of the *Trieste*. The craft was assigned to the U.S. Navy Electronics Laboratory of the Bureau of Ships, located at San Diego, California, where it arrived in August 1958. NEL scientists promptly launched a major deep-submergence research program that is still continuing. During the program the *Trieste* became the only non-commissioned vessel ever to receive a unit commendation. Scientific observers who have dived in *Trieste* include geologist Robert F. Dill, biologist Eric G. Barham, geologist Edwin L. Hamilton, geologist David G. Moore, and acoustician Kenneth V. Mackenzie, chief scientist in charge of the deep-submergence program. Oceanographic scientists working on and helping shape the *Trieste* program—which is purely and entirely scientific research—include Dr. Ralph J. Christensen, technical director, NEL, and Dr. Gilbert H. Curl, coordinator for ocean science.

For six years, from 1958 to 1964, or until the arrival of deep-diving submarines, the *Trieste* was the only American craft capable of descending deeper than the Navy's nuclear submarines.

The *Trieste* works much like the balloon that carried Professor Auguste Piccard into the stratosphere. A balloon has its bag filled with a gas that is lighter than air; therefore the balloon rises in air. The *Trieste* has her float—the biggest part of her, the long oblong section—filled with a liquid that is lighter than seawater. The liquid used aboard the *Trieste* is aviation gasoline, 34,000 gallons of it; consequently the *Trieste* normally rises in water. But, as a balloon has ballast to help pull it down, so does *Trieste*. She carries 16 tons of small steel pellets in two separate containers. When the ballast is dropped, *Trieste* climbs to the surface. The two tubs of metal pellets are located in the fore and aft sections of the *Trieste*'s float. The pellets are held back by an electromagnet at each opening; when they are switched off, the ballast is dropped into the sea.

The balloon carries its passengers in a basket or gondola beneath it. So does *Trieste,* except that it is called a pressure hull, or observation sphere. The pressure hull is a steel ball. For deep research, as at the bottom of the Challenger Deep, there is a Krupp-machined steel hull with walls 5½ inches thick, built to withstand a pressure of more than eight tons per square inch. For shallower depths, to 20,000 feet, the *Trieste* uses a Terni pressure hull.

Operating controls are inside the pressure hull, where the pilot and one or two observers sit. The observation window, or view port, is made of 6-inch-thick Plexiglas. "It looks forward and slightly downward and provides the scientists with an unusually good view of the sea floor just a few inches from their eyes," the Electronics Laboratory says.

The *Trieste,* 67 feet long and 15 feet wide, has a draft of 13 feet. She is one of the two bathyscaphes in the world that can reach the deepest bottom of the ocean. The other one is the French *Archimède.* A third bathyscaphe, the *F.N.R.S. 3,* has an operating depth of 13,500 feet, or less than three miles. No deep-diving submarines can go down nearly so deep as the *Trieste* and the *Archimède.* Bathyscaphes, again like balloons, are fundamentally elevators that only take men up and down. They are extremely limited in their ability to navigate. *Trieste*'s battery-driven motors pushed her over the bottom for only 6 hours at a speed of only one knot. One of the hopes of oceanographers for the 1970's is a bathyscaphe with a range of 30 miles.

Trieste has been remodeled and improved by the Navy, and she is now known as *Trieste II*. The changes were made to enable *Trieste II* to assist the Navy's Deep Submergence program. She is the flagship of the group now studying for the Navy the deepest regions of the oceans and how to operate in them, and evolving the future deep-diving rescue, search, and recovery submarines (Chapter 11). There has been added to *Trieste II* a new Westinghouse "side-looking" sonar that continuously looks out at the ocean floor to right and left of her line of travel. The Sperry Rand Corporation has provided two other additions to *Trieste II* to assist her in underwater maneuvering: a Doppler sonar to measure her movement with respect to the sea floor, and a microelectronic computer enabling the pilot to make complex changes of her position at the touch of a button. On the old *Trieste,* because of her extremely slow speed, ocean currents could cause navigational errors. The computer will allow for the currents, and help *Trieste II* navigate more accurately. Her speed of two knots is double that of the old *Trieste.*

The world's other bathyscaphe with the ability to reach the deepest sea floor, the *Archimède,* has also been active. In 1964 she reached, for the first time, the deepest place in the Atlantic, the Puerto Rico Trench. The men aboard her included French Navy Lieutenant Huet de Froberville, pilot of the bathyscaphe; Lieutenant Marc Menez, technician; and Dr. Henri Delauze, chief of the French Bathyscaphe Laboratory, scientist.

The *Archimède* altogether made ten trips into the Puerto Rico Trench. On her first, May 4, 1964, she reached 17,700 feet—the deepest penetration to that date of the Atlantic. She took 7 hours for the trip, and traveled about 1½ miles along the south wall of the trench.

She got all the way to the bottom, 27,510 feet below the surface, on the second dive. Here her crew saw fish 1 to 5 inches long swimming past. They saw pinky-white fish that swam around like tendrils, some of them 9 inches wide; they saw five or six fish together. They found an abundance of fish both along the bottom of the trench and along its walls. They also found previously un-known currents more than 20,000 feet deep, took rock samples, and made stroboscopic pictures. Like many voyages of discovery, those of the *Archimède* resulted in a mystery: There are gigantic steps forming both walls of the Puerto Rico Trench. What is the explanation for the steps? How were they made?

Dr. Maurice Ewing of Columbia University was coordinator of Operation Deepscan, as the journeys into the Puerto Rico Trench were called. The trench, 70 miles north of Puerto Rico, is 450 miles long and 27,510 feet deep. The abyssal plain at its bottom is 150 miles long. Besides Columbia University, those supporting the *Archimède* off Puerto Rico were the French Navy; the National Scientific Research Center of France; Woods Hole; and the U.S. Navy Electronics Laboratory.

In 1962, the *Archimède* carried French deep-sea explorers nearly six miles down into the Pacific's Kurile-Kamchatka Trench, the second-deepest dive in man's history, surpassed only by that of the U.S. Navy's *Trieste* in the Challenger Deep. The *Archimède* reached 31,350 feet down, near northern Japan, where French Commander Georges Houot and Navy engineer Pierre Henri Willm saw what they called "intensive life." The bottom, they said, was "very cozy." They, too, found a previously unknown current.

The first bathyscaphe of all was the *F.N.R.S. 2*. The *F.N.R.S. 1* was a balloon that hoisted Auguste Piccard into the stratosphere. "F.N.R.S." stands for Fonds National de la Recherche Scientifique, the Belgian Scientific Research Fund that supported Auguste Pic-card's inventions.

On November 3, 1948, the *F.N.R.S. 2,* the first vessel ever designed to descend untethered into the ocean depths, did so for the first time. There were no men inside her. She descended to 4,500 feet and returned by herself. Instruments aboard her proved she had gone down that far.

On a series of dives in August 1953, the *F.N.R.S. 2* took French Lieutenant Commander Georges Houot and Lieutenant Pierre Henri Willm to one of men's coveted goals: They were the first to dive a full mile down and so beat the records of William Beebe and Otis Barton. "My aim was clear," said Willm, "to pass through the 600- to 1,000-foot layer of water in which the submarine is king and to penetrate a world as yet unknown." Boarding the bathyscaphe, Houot—this was back in 1953, remember—had a thought: "The first explorers of interstellar space," he said to Willm, "will shut themselves up in just the same way."

At 2,000 feet down, Willm said, the men saw "a dazzling sight": "A spiral medusa, a kind of jellyfish, with a translucent body striped with orange rose up in front of us. It was at least three feet in length. This long spring of jelly, like a coiled-up eel, rhythmically stretched and contracted."

At 2,600 feet, said Houot, "The microorganisms passed more rapidly. . . . I could not help reflecting on the abundance of life to be seen. [There was] as much evidence of life at 2,400 feet as at 1,000 feet from the surface."

At 9:30 A.M. on August 12, 1953, Houot glanced at his pressure gauge: 3,500 feet. Below 4,300 feet, a luminous animal bumped a porthole and emitted a shower of sparks. "We have gone deeper than Beebe!" he thought. At 9:55 they reached 5,115 feet and started up. "No human being had been down to this depth before," said Houot. "We were 560 deeper than (Otis) Barton had been, and our sphere was moving almost without perceptible motion."

On a later dive, Houot and Willm reached over a mile: to a depth of 6,890 feet. Returned on the surface, the *F.N.R.S. 2* had to be towed home through heavy seas. This was too much for the bathyscaphe. She might dive deep, but on the surface she broke up.

Houot and Willm's world's record for a deep dive lasted till the next month. On September 30, 1953, in the second bathyscaphe to be constructed, the *Trieste,* Auguste Piccard and his son Jacques got to the bottom of the Tyrrhenian Trench, in the Mediterranean, about 50 miles from the island of Ponza. The Piccards dived 10,330 feet down.

In December, 1953, off Dakar, on the westernmost coast of Africa, the *F.N.R.S. 3*—the third bathyscaphe ever to be built— made a series of dives. Jacques-Yves Cousteau went along with Houot on one to 4,000 feet. At 2,500 feet, Houot said, "There were medusae swimming among long, translucent filaments. They were escorted by eels. . . . At the limit of our field of vision there were brilliant dancing specks."

Below 3,500 feet there were big squids. "As they crossed the illuminated area (from the bathyscaphe's floodlights)," said Houot, "each one reacted by discharging its ink. Spear fishermen know of this defense mechanism of the squid: It emits a whitish and faintly phosphorescent cloud which assumes a shape resembling that of its own body. The enemy mistakes the cloud for its prey and swoops down upon it, allowing the squid to escape." As the bathyscaphe sank farther, it went through a world, Houot reported, "that seethed with shrimps, squids, and fish of all sorts." At 4,000 feet, the *F.N.R.S. 3* reached the bottom: a bed of sand. The men were not alone. Cousteau exclaimed, "A shark!" Said Houot, "I find myself nose to nose with a placid beast at least six feet long, which contemplated us with bulbous eyes and then, with a flick of its tail, glided majestically away." Altogether, three sharks showed up; their shadows made them look enormous.

On a deeper dive, on the sea floor 7,000 feet down, the men in the *F.N.R.S. 3* took photographs that cleared up a zoological mystery. The benthosaurus, a fish, has three long fins whose use scientists did not know. The photographs showed that the fish sits or rests on the bottom on its fins, which spread out like a tripod.

On February 15, 1954, still off Dakar, Africa, Houot and Willm descended 2½ miles, or 13,287 feet, almost the *F.N.R.S. 3*'s rated depth. They saw multitudes of small sea creatures "like a snowstorm in reverse." At nearly 10,000 feet, there were swarms of shrimps and organisms resembling siphonophores. A bit lower, there were medusae. The bottom, 2½ miles down, was described by Houot: "I looked out in fascination. A sea anemone emerged from the sand—an ethereal vision; the current swayed it gently on its stem. What a strange sight! If I hadn't known, I should have sworn it was a flower, or at least a plant. A white corolla a few inches wide and a hand's breadth in height was spreading out at the top of a stem a foot tall. It looked like a tulip. In reality it was made up of a colony of little animals attached to the soil, a type of sea anemone. . . ." A shark came out. It had, said Willm, "a fine big head. He's quite different from the sharks on the surface."

"And so," said Philippe Tailliez after this dive, "the age of the bathyscaphe has come. This ship of the deep, which few men believed possible, is now a reality."

More was to come. In 1959, Dr. Andreas B. Rechnitzer and Jacques Piccard managed to reach 18,450 feet; in 1960, they got to 23,000 feet. The *Trieste* (now the *Trieste II*) and the *Archimède* have added further convincing proof that the ship of the deep is here. In spite of their explorations to date, they have only just begun their task: to explore the most unreachable, darkest, coldest, most hazardous zone of the ocean, its deepest region.

The depths of the ocean below 20,000 feet, the deepest region, which can be penetrated only by men in bathyscaphes or by the deepest trawls such as those of the *Galathea*, is called the hadal zone. This comes from the Greek "Hades," which means either hell, the abode of the dead, or a gloomy subterranean realm beyond the western ocean.

The greatest depths of the sea—all areas in the sea a mile deep, or deeper, excepting only those of the Arctic—are one uninterrupted region; they join each other. The deep waters of the Atlantic, Pacific, and Indian basins meet those of the Antarctic Ocean, which completely surrounds the Antarctic continent and so girdles the earth. Thus the deep waters form one continuous great unexplored area. The plains of the hadal zone are vast. Yet the hadal zone is dotted with sea mounts and divided by mountain ranges. And the deep waters include the great trenches—gashes so deep that they are cut off from the rest of the sea floor.

The hadal zone was for centuries believed to be without life of any kind. This was for two main reasons: Conditions in it—the dark, the frigid cold, the pressure—are so appalling to us that we did not see how any life could exist in the hadal zone; and we had no equipment either to trawl up specimens from the hadal zone or to send eyewitnesses down into it.

Now that we have sent trawls and visited the deepest sea, one thing stands out: Conditions may seem to be almost impossible for life in the hadal zone, but nobody has told this to the animals that live there.

So far, only five fishes, C. P. Idyll says, including the deepest fish caught—the brotulid taken by the *Galathea* at 23,400 feet in the Sunda Deep—have been identified in the hadal zone below 20,000 feet. (He wrote this before the *Archimède* explored the Puerto Rico Trench.) Known fish in the hadal zone also include stomiatoids, angler fish, gulpers, and the flatfish observed from the *Trieste*. But animals other than fish brought up in the deepest trawls are plentiful; Torben Wolff, a scientist aboard the *Galathea,* listed 310 species from the hadal zone. Besides fish, there are sea cucumbers, sea urchins, clams, snails, sea spiders, small crustaceans, worms, jellyfish, sponges. Plantlike animals, the sea pens and gorgonians, or sea fans, appear to abound in the deep sea. They may grow huge there: Some sea pens, Mr. Idyll says, that are ordinarily about a foot tall, grow to about 8 feet in the great depths.

The stomiatoids, fish which are known to reach up to 6 feet long, have rows of portholelike organs along their sides, red and green light organs below their well-developed eyes, and luminous filaments (chin or throat whiskers) that light up and may stream out many times the length of the fish. The viperfish, one of the stomiatoids, has teeth so large it can't close its mouth over them, and so the teeth remain outside when the mouth is shut. There is a gulper with a whiplike tail. A red light on the tail apparently lures prey toward the gulper, which may sweep its tail back and forth in enticing fashion. No man has observed the gulper in action. But a gulper was netted by Sir Alister Hardy with its tail tightly coiled around the filaments of a small animal also caught in the net; so it is believed the gulper winds its tail around its victim.

One of the gulpers is 6 feet long. Another gulper is 2 feet long. A deep angler fish is 3 feet long. We do not know what other fish or animals may be in the deep sea. "Certainly it would not be surprising," says C. P. Idyll, "if large, agile animals were able to avoid the clumsy gear with which oceanographers have so far sampled the deep sea. We know for sure that specimens of some creatures of the depths have not yet been caught, for no one has hauled to the surface the 6-foot fishes of which Beebe got such tantalizing glimpses from the bathysphere off Bermuda. And of course Beebe was by no means in the true deep sea; we have no way of knowing whether not only 6-foot fish but perhaps 60-foot fish may live there, someday to be snared by an astonished and triumphant scientist."

Mr. Idyll almost echoes the scientist who believed in the sea serpent, the late Anton Bruun. Says Mr. Idyll: "In our present state of knowledge we cannot yet abandon the possibility that some as-yet-unknown monsters exist in the deep sea."

Future trips of *Trieste II* or any other bathyscaphe will bring before our eyes new information on geography and geology of the ocean floor. T. F. Gaskell, in *Under the Deep Oceans*, says a bathyscaphe eyewitness can explore the floor as men never could before, ". . . he can see the whole picture of what is around him . . . and he can move himself toward interesting objects in order to gain a better view."

Dr. Gaskell, a British Petroleum oceanographer, was the chief scientist aboard when the Challenger Deep was discovered. For years the Philippine Trench had been believed to be the deepest hole on earth. Then, one day in 1952, the British oceanographic research ship *Challenger* was steaming south from Japan over the Marianas Trench. Dr. Gaskell wanted to carry on some seismic experiments. He had John Swallow set off small explosions and listen for the echoes from the sea floor to his hydrophone. The soundings rapidly increased: over 5,000 fathoms (30,000 feet), 5,663 fathoms (33,978 feet)—this was exciting; it was nearly as deep as any sounding previously recorded; 5,889 fathoms (35,334 feet)—a new world's record depth.

The first British *Challenger* expedition, which had probed the depths of the seas from 1872 to 1876, and thus established the science of oceanography, had paid out overboard marked rope to measure depth. Her deepest sounding (by rope) was 4,500 fathoms (27,000 feet) in the Marianas Trench, near where the second *Challenger* found her deepest hole.

From the time of the first *Challenger* to the second one a number of deeper and deeper spots were located. The U.S.S. *Tuscarora,* the first ship to use piano wire (not rope) to measure depths, was out on a voyage at the time of the original *Challenger* and found 4,655 fathoms (27,930 feet) east of the Kurile Islands. The first sounding past 5,000 fathoms (30,000 feet) was by the British *Penguin* in 1895. She found 5,155 fathoms (30,930 feet) in the Kermadec Trench northeast of New Zealand. The German *Planet* and the Dutch *Willebord* (using sounding methods, not a rope or wire) found 5,539 fathoms (33,234 feet) in the Philippine Trench. The U.S.S. *Ramapo* found 5,673 fathoms (34,038 feet) in the Japan Trench. Then the German *Emden* found 5,686 fathoms (34,116 feet) in the Philippine Trench.

Harry H. Hess, a Princeton University professor who is now a rear admiral in the Naval Reserve, was commander of a large fleet oiler, the U.S.S. *Cape Johnson,* during World War II. He found a depth of 5,740 fathoms (34,440 feet) in the Philippine Trench. This is now known as the Cape Johnson Deep. It was from near here that the *Galathea* dredged up her sea anemones, worms, bacteria, and other specimens from the bottom.

Then, in 1952, came the discovery, by the second *Challenger,* of the new Challenger Deep.

Jacques Piccard and Robert Dietz at once wanted men to see the Challenger Deep with their own eyes. "Yes, it must be done," said Piccard. "Dietz and I discussed this together and agreed that we had to do it. . . . Until man placed himself on the bottom of the deepest depression on earth he would not be satisfied."

So, in 1960, the Challenger Deep was plumbed by men—by Jacques Piccard and Lieutenant Don Walsh in the U.S. Navy's *Trieste*. Their dive, however, will probably not stand as the journey to the deepest bottom on the sea. In 1959, the Soviet research ship *Vitiaz* had found a depth of 36,198 feet in the Marianas Trench, and in 1962 the British research ship *Cook* topped (or bottomed) the *Vitiaz*'s record by finding the Cook Deep, 37,782 feet, over 7 miles, in the Mindanao Trench, near the Philippines. What is happening is that ships, especially naval and oceanographic vessels, are equipped with continually new, better, more sensitive echo sounders, which can probe increasingly deeper. As I am writing this chapter, a news story by Jim Bishop has appeared, stating that a depth finder aboard the U.S. carrier *Midway* can register up to 7,000 fathoms (42,000 feet). The *Midway* has the potential to locate a deeper trench than any yet found.

Jacques Piccard may be the man to explore any deeper trenches that may be discovered. Today he works with the Grumman Aircraft and Engineering Corporation. He plans a bigger, better bathyscaphe that will carry 3 or 4 men to any depth for days at a time, and will be able to roam over the ocean floor. "It is," says Piccard, "quite feasible now."

PART
VII

Some Mysteries of the Depths

CHAPTER
22

*What Animals Make
the Deep Scattering Layer?*

"THE RECENT DISCOVERY that a living cloud of some unknown creatures is spread over much of the ocean at a depth of several hundred fathoms below the surface is the most exciting thing that has been learned about the ocean for many years."

The quotation is from Rachel L. Carson's book, *The Sea Around Us.* The book appeared in 1950. Scientists of that year were not sure exactly what the unknown creatures were that made up the living cloud. Ever since, there have been efforts to find out. Scientists still are not sure. The deep scattering layer, as the living cloud is called, has become one of the major mysteries of the sea.

Because the sea is dark and hides in it whatever is beneath the surface, most of what we know about the depths and bottom of the sea has come from the use of sound. Until the 1920's we did not even use sound. The way to measure the depth of the water under a ship was to drop over the side a rope or wire with a weight attached and see how much line had to be paid out before the weight touched bottom. Then echo sounding was first used. In echo sounding, you send out a noise from a source fixed beneath the hull of a ship. The source today is likely to be in a dome protruding from the ship's bottom. The noise, in a modern echo sounder, is a pulse of high-pitched sound. Aboard ship, you listen for its echo. You know the speed of sound waves through the water. The time it takes for the echo to return from the sea floor enables you to estimate the depth of the water. Sound waves also can penetrate layers of sediment or rocks beneath the sea floor. The sound travels at different speeds through different substances. Echoes returning fractions of seconds apart therefore indicate what the bottom is composed of. This whole process is now automatic, and an echo sounder can draw a rough picture of the sea bottom as a ship sails along—a tracing drawn on a roll of paper, determined by the returning echoes.

During World War II echo sounders were installed in many ships to help locate enemy submarines, whose air-filled hulls bounced back strong echoes. Today echo sounders are used routinely in hundreds of ships. They are always switched on when a ship approaches shallow seas to guard against running aground and as an aid to locating exactly the ship's position. Frequently they are left turned on all the time, with the result that they draw a continuous profile of the ocean floor. Most submerged sea mountains and valleys have been discovered by echo sounding.

No one at first expected echo sounders to locate life in the sea, but they did. In the 1930's operators of early echo sounders learned that some sound waves were coming back not from the sea floor but from floating objects located between the ship and the bottom: presumably fish, whales, and so on. One echo might be reflected by something unknown halfway down, a later echo might be received from the bottom. By the 1930's, therefore, fishermen began thinking about using sound equipment to locate schools of fish. Today improved echo sounders are used to find herring, sprat, and cod.

During World War II, in deep water not far off the coast of California, Navy echo sounders encountered for the first time Miss Carson's "most exciting thing." Something unexplained in the water reflected—and scattered—the sound. It is now called the deep scattering layer, or DSL for short.

Three scientists, Miss Carson reported, D. F. Eyring, R. J. Christensen, and R. W. Waitt, aboard the U.S.S. *Jasper* in 1942, were using sound equipment. It echoed back, indicating there was a widespread layer of some sort hanging between the keel of the ship and the seabed, which returned an echo to their sound waves. It was from 1,000 to 1,500 feet below the surface. The layer was found over an area 300 miles wide.

In 1945 Martin W. Johnson, a marine biologist of the Scripps Institution of Oceanography, made a further discovery. Aboard the vessel *E. W. Scripps,* Johnson observed that the layer, whatever it was, moved up and down. It moved up near the surface at night, and moved down deep during the day. "This discovery," says Miss Carson, "disposed of speculations that the reflections came from something inanimate, perhaps a mere physical discontinuity in the water, and showed that the layer is composed of living creatures capable of controlled movement." The scattering layer, that is to say, was not caused by a difference of temperature, density, or salinity in layers of water.

More observations quickly followed. The U.S.S. *Henderson* in 1947 encountered the layer from 900 to 2,700 feet deep, all the way from San Diego to the Antarctic. From San Diego to Yokosuka, Japan, the *Henderson* later found the layer like a giant blanket almost across the Pacific. In the summer of 1947 the U.S.S. *Nereus,* operating her fathometer all the way from Pearl Harbor to the Arctic, located the scattering layer in all the deep water she traversed, then found another surprise: there were two layers, one above the other.

Since then the layers have been found to exist almost everywhere in the seas except in the Arctic and Antarctic Oceans. More than two layers have been spotted; sometimes there are three or even five.

The postwar British research ship *Challenger* ran into the scattering layer. As she steamed up the North American west coast, in water shown on charts to be 12,000 feet deep, she kept getting echoes indicating very shallow soundings. Finally she stopped. Her echo sounder indicated the sea bottom beneath her keel was rising right up. T. F. Gaskell, the oceanographer who helped with the finding of the Challenger Deep, commented: "Now a change in depth is not unreasonable if a ship is traveling over the seabed, but for the bottom to move while the ship was in one place was highly irregular."

Three principal theories as to what the scattering layer—or layers—was made of were quickly proposed. It was suggested that these layers were composed of:

(1) Plankton. Many of these tiny creatures are known to move upward in the nighttime. An objection: many plankters (creatures of the plankton) are not notably good sound reflectors.

(2) Fish. Many fish have air bladders that make them good reflectors of sound waves. An air bladder returns a strong echo. Its air space acts as a resonator and gives a much stronger echo in water than anything else. An air bladder also helps a fish adjust its buoyancy and so rise or sink. Even small and widely scattered fish with air bladders might explain the observed echoes.

(3) Squid. According to this theory, some of the 10-armed relatives of the octopus live far below the lighted upper waters of the sea and, after dark, raid the plankton-rich surface water. Squid come in all sizes. Big ones are the principal food of the sperm whale, found in all temperate and tropical waters. Squid also are eaten by the bottle-nosed whale, by most other toothed whales, by seals, and by sea birds. Are squid abundant enough to form the deep scattering layer?

An early effort was made to take pictures of the scattering layer. Gunnar Rollefson, a Norwegian biologist, lowered a camera into a sound-reflecting layer 120 to 150 feet down. He got pictures of moving fish including a cod.

Scientists from Woods Hole tried to sample the layer. They towed plankton nets through it. They collected deep-water plankton, euphausid shrimp, and glassworms. But is the layer composed of larger animals feeding on the shrimp—animals too fast or too wary or too big for plankton nets?

William Beebe, back in the 1930's, had thought he saw more life from his bathysphere than man had imagined in the depths. A quarter of a mile down, he reported living creatures "as thick as I have ever seen them." A half mile down, he saw a mist of plankton swirling in his light. For many years, many scientists have believed, and many still do, that animals thin out—become far fewer—as the sea gets deeper. Beebe was never sure he believed this after his deep dives. He questioned it.

During one investigation of the scattering layer off Newfoundland, a rorqual whale surfaced almost alongside the investigating ship, thus suggesting that a large animal might find food in the layer. T. F. Gaskell commented in *Under the Deep Oceans* (1960): "The most probable explanation of the phenomenon is that a large concentration of small light-sensitive plants or animals (the plankton, that is) accumulates and moves up and down to maintain the brightness of light that is desirable for growth. Larger animals, like the sea shrimps, feed on the layer, and possibly sometimes even larger fish eat the shrimps." The shrimp—plus or minus other air-bladder-carrying fish—could be the ones that reflect the sound. There also can be any number of nonreflecting organisms right in among those that turn back the sound.

Another theory was put forward in 1951 by N. B. Marshall, today Senior Principal Scientific Officer at the British Museum (Natural History). Previously, it had been believed that bathypelagic fish, which do make extensive climbs in the sea, had no air bladder. Bathypelagic fish, which swim in midocean depths, include rattails, brotulids, bristlemouths, hatchetfish, lantern fish, and others. Most are small, around 3 inches long. Many have turned out, in recent research, to have air bladders. "At least half the bathypelagic fishes," Marshall has said, "notably many stomiatoid and lantern fishes, have a well-developed swim bladder." Marshall accordingly suggested they might cause the scattering layer; their migration upward appears about the right length, and, besides, these fish are not to be found in the Arctic or Antarctic, where the deep scattering layer is not found either. If Marshall is right, Sir Alister Hardy, the Oxford University zoologist and author of a comprehensive work on plankton, *The Open Sea*, comments, "These little fish, which rush up towards the surface at night, are not only in very much larger numbers than we had ever imagined, but they must also be distributed remarkably evenly through the oceans." Beebe, from his observations through the window of his bathysphere, had already said that he thought these fish were indeed much more numerous than our net collections made us believe. Said he: "Our big tow-nets are towed only very slowly through the water; it would not be surprising if the great majority of these very actively swimming fish were to make their escape through the large mouth of the net and leave only a small sample behind."

Jacques-Ives Cousteau took Harold Edgerton of the Massachusetts Institute of Technology out to photograph the scattering layer. Edgerton, who had invented stroboscopic high-speed photography, was nicknamed Papa Flash by Cousteau.

Cousteau reported:

> We found a number of deep-sea monsters in the deep scattering layer. True, they were only small, silver-plated *Argyropelecus,* or hatchetfish, but a photo enlargement of their bulging eyes, saber-toothed-tiger jaws, and bellies covered with luminous nodules would scare a side-show crowd.
>
> A deep-scattering-layer station in the Villefranche canyon produced an astonishing inventory from a stratum 100 feet thick and 1,000 feet down. The statistical evidence was that there was one pretty medusa (a jellyfish) per cubic yard in this deep scattering layer. Evening shots showed them all oriented upward—they were rising. In the morning pictures their crowns were inverted—they were going down. They were accompanied by crustaceans, arrow worms, and other unidentified creatures in the endless rise and fall of life layers.

Then Cousteau and Edgerton were startled by the result of their picture taking:

> Farther down, darkness prevailed day and night and we did not expect such a density of animals. Yet when we put Edgerton's cameras in the black depths, we found that *density of plankton increased* below the deep scattering layer, in the 2,300- to 3,500-foot level, but this did not show on the echo sounder. The photographs were crammed with white corpuscles—the very image of outer space as seen through a large reflecting telescope. I remembered that two men—and two only—Dr. William Beebe and Otis Barton—had seen this layer with their own eyes from Barton's bathysphere. Both had reported that the density of micro-organisms increased with depth. Science had paid no attention to this upsetting datum. Our cameras seemed to confirm it.

Few large animals showed up in midwater pictures.

> I found an explanation for this [Cousteau said] in the Indian Ocean. One evening the sonar graph reported a very thick scattering layer in 400 feet of water. I stopped *Calypso* [his ship] and shot Edgerton's camera into it. I watched the [camera] sink down the graph paper. As it neared the deep scattering layer, the thick trace vanished. I had the winch-man continue lowering deeper. The 400-foot-deep scattering layer returned to life as thick as before, erasing the camera's image. Here were animals that quickly dodged the alien camera and reassembled when it went deeper. I could not believe they were the usual feeble medusas or difting plankton and siphonophores. The flash may have alerted them, or perhaps the faint hum of the camera motor, sounding like a fire alarm to them, or even the slight pressure waves ahead of the descending rig. At any rate, here was proof that closely packed, fast-moving creatures also formed a deep scattering layer.

Cousteau and Edgerton sailed again with new cameras and a new photolab aboard *Calypso* for immediate looks at pictures. "Plenty of little animals" showed on the film. Said Cousteau,

> the enlargements presented a new riddle. Many of the dots were blurred. Looking closer, we saw that they had comet tails. Edgerton's electronic flash lasted about three-thousandths of a second, and the "bugs" [the little animals] were 1 to 4 inches from the lens. He computed that they were traveling at a velocity of 3 to 10 feet per second! Even the midges of the ocean were fully capable of dodging the camera. High-speed micro-organisms and athletic fish alike kept clear of lowered instruments. Where did this leave the oceanographers who relied on plankton nets to give them an idea of life distribution in the dark below?

Next Cousteau and Edgerton built a camera on a glider that could be towed deep in the water by *Calypso* and, they hoped, would sneak silently up on the inhabitants of the depths. "The first tests of the camera glider produced plenty of empty black water," Cousteau said, "but from time to time we surprised dense assemblies of shrimps and obtained a movie of a deep school of squids dispersing into flight 12 feet ahead of the camera. Now we were breaking through into the bigger mobile crowd in the deep scattering layer."

Cousteau noted that in the Mediterranean he found the deep scattering layer 1,500 feet down. He had no suspicion there might be even more layers beneath that one till he reached Madeira, "a small mountain range marooned far at sea, crowded with 270,000 people dependent for life upon a deep-sea monster, a single species of fish, *Asphanopus carbo* or the espada." The 10-pound espada, Cousteau says, "looked something like a black barracuda with fiery glints on its hide. It had saber teeth and huge green eyes. The espada, the only deep-sea monstrosity of economic significance, has been fished only near Madeira." Then a Portuguese skipper told him a surprising fact: While the espada harvest is virtually the same night after night after night, men fish at different depths, depending on the moon, to make their catch. In other words, the layer of espada, around a mile down, rises and falls according to the moonlight. But no moonlight—no light at all, in fact—penetrates to a depth of a mile. Cousteau wondered if the espada's climb was not dependent upon climbs of other creatures above it. Plankton and fish might be in the scattering layer at the top, for example, in a layer that is reached by light rays; then something underneath that eats the plankton and fish and chases them up; and so on down till the third layer or so, which would be the espada eating whatever was above it.

At Woods Hole J. B. Hersey and others studied different fish sounds, learned to distinguish between many of them, then developed a combination camera and echo sounder to photograph fish making a specific sound. This has resulted in the belief that most of the echoes from the deep scattering layer are from the swim bladders of enormous quantities of small fish from 1 to 6 inches long (N. B. Marshall's bathypelagic fish).

With men now entering the depths of the sea, scientists can at last obtain what they really need: some long looks at the scattering layer itself. In 1954 two French naval officers, Lieutenant Commander Georges Houot and Lieutenant Pierre Willm, along with Jacques-Yves Cousteau, made a series of dives in a bathyscaphe. What they saw explained nothing and only added to the mystery of the deep scattering layer. Said Cousteau, "So far as we can see, there is, biologically speaking, no deep scattering layer, but rather a great bowl of living soup extended on down and growing thicker the deeper into the 'tureen' we go."

But where would the energy necessary for life come from in the depths—energy that surface life gets from sunlight and plant plankton? "There must," says Cousteau, "be somewhere an unsuspected link in the cycle of marine life yet to be discovered."

Cousteau described further the concentration of life he saw from the bathyscaphe: "I have the feeling that I am looking at the Milky Way during a beautiful summer night." Sir Alister Hardy thought that the reason Cousteau did not see the scattering layer was that it scampered away at the approach of the strange bathyscaphe, as it had seemed to dash away from Dr. Harold Edgerton's camera. Or the layer may not have scampered. The animals do not necessarily have to be thickly disposed, Richard Backus of Woods Hole tells me, to produce the observed echoes.

In 1962 off California, where the scattering layer had been first discovered, a young naval oceanographer, Dr. Eric G. Barham, peered through a porthole into the dark waters. He was aboard the bathyscaphe *Trieste*. Dr. Barham got into scattering-layer depths; generally three layers are present off California. When the sun is high, they are at about 950 feet, 1,400 feet, and 1,700 feet down. A layer may be 150- to 500-feet thick. Dr. Barham saw small, ghostlike figures before his porthole. They were, he discovered, siphonophores. Siphonophores are floating jellyfishlike animals. The Portuguese man-of-war is the most famous siphonophore. Siphonophores are many-armed and largely transparent. They reach a size of more than two feet long, dwell in the open sea, and have gas-filled chambers that, Dr. Barham believes, reflect sound. The chambers, when inflated, cause the siphonophores to rise.

"Siphonophores," says Dr. Barham, "fulfill all the prerequisites of a major scattering organism." He believes they may have been the original scattering layer discovered off California as well as many others found since.

There are in the sea enormous concentrations of life: The vast aggregations, in schools, of herring, cod, and mackerel; swarms of salpa (transparent, barrel-shaped stockfish); and such great numbers of one copepod, *Calanus finmarchicus*, that the sea is colored brown by them. Concentrations of dinoflagellates (tiny plants) cause the red tide near Florida, India, Japan, California, and Chile;

they color the Red Sea, and they cause pink icebergs. Minute plants called coccolithophores (5 million to a quart) turn the sea white or milky. Most pertinent of all, one siphonophore, velella, is known to form huge swarms. The individuals in a swarm may be many feet apart. One concentration of velella, according to *Ecological Animal Geography*, extended for 300 kilometers (187 miles).

Velella has a small triangular sail atop its float; wind striking the sail blows it along, hence it is called the before-the-wind sailor. Velella is cast on shore by the thousands. In the Atlantic the float of the common species is only two inches long.

Dan Merriman of Yale University's Bingham Oceanographic Laboratory told me of the tremendous concentrations of life in the Humboldt Current, the northward-flowing current off the coast of Peru. Merriman has explored the Humboldt. "One morning," he said, "we saw birds working over the sea—thousands of them. Those birds had come to feed on anchovetas (anchovy-sized fish). The anchovetas were chased by jacks (bigger fish). The jacks circled so the tiny fish were close together. You could see the jacks snapping up their meal.

"There wasn't any water there. You could have got out and walked on the fish." It is, Dan Merriman says, impossible to exaggerate the abundance of life in the Humboldt.

As proof, if any is needed, Yale's Ed Migdalski, Merriman, and Wendell Anderson caught a 3,300-pound manta ray in the Humboldt. The manta is the great flat ray of the surface of the sea (18 feet across its wings). A relative of the shark, it consumes tiny plankton and animal life. It leaps 15 feet or higher out of the open sea, sometimes somersaults, and bellyflops onto the surface with crashes like peals of thunder. "They splash," says Merriman, "as if the Empire State Building had dropped into the sea." No one knows why the manta rays leap. Says Merriman: "You know, if I could jump like that, I'd do it all the time, just for the fun of it." Another jumper the Yale men saw in the Humboldt Current was the spinner shark. "I saw three spinner sharks on one day,"

Merriman recalls, "or maybe it was the same one jumping three times, I don't know which. These weigh a hundred pounds or more, jump out of the water, travel through the air a way, and then re-enter. As they sail through the air they revolve, end around end, head around tail, like a wheel spinning parallel to the water."

Also sighted in the Humboldt by Sally Wheatland of Yale, Jim Morrow, and others were: blackfish (small whales), the sperm whale, the white shark (the man-eater notorious in Australia), sea lions, squid, marlin, sailfish, tuna, mako sharks, rooster fish, bonito, Spanish mackerel, blue runners, jacks, and dolphins. Wendell Anderson, on this same trip, hauled in a 797-pound black marlin out of this current teeming with life.

Another kind of concentration of animal life that occurs in the sea is the occasional swarming of usually scarce creatures. In August 1951, for instance, the Japanese squid was so common south of Sakhalin that five tons were caught in one net. Thousands of squid were washed ashore on Scottish beaches in 1937; at one place, there were 668 in a little over 2 miles. In 1950 and 1951, octopuses swarmed in Europe, especially off France: One man looked out to a rough sea and counted 25 octopuses. Back in the winter of 1899–1900, a French beach near Cherbourg Peninsula, near where American troops landed in World War II, was littered with octopuses: at one place there were 68 in 200 yards. Before 1899, the Marine Biological Station at Plymouth, England, was offering a reward for each octopus caught; in 1900, octopuses swarmed and caused disastrous losses to fishermen by eating crabs and lobsters by the thousands. In 1955 only one specimen of *Tremoctopus violaceus*, an octopus, was caught in the northern Adriatic Sea; in 1956 it appeared by the tens of thousands. And in 1956 more octopuses appeared off South Australia than ever before. In *Kingdom of the Octopus* Frank W. Lane reports these surprising and temporary concentrations of sea life.

I am indebted to Dr. Charles E. Lane, professor of Marine Sciences at the Marine Laboratory of the University of Miami, for information that the purple-and-blue Portuguese man-of-war, with its stinging tentacles 100 feet or so in length, is sometimes the animal that most troubles skin divers in the sea near Miami. The stingers contain a poison said to be almost as potent as a cobra's venom. The men-of-war visit Miami (as the human tourists do) mostly in the winter. In 1964 a 73-year-old swimmer was killed by man-of-war stings off Miami Beach.

Late in the summer of 1965 the Portuguese man-of-war swarmed on the East Coast of the United States from Montauk Point, Long Island, to Chincoteague, Virginia. On Long Island more than a hundred bathers were stung, none seriously.

Eric Barham was not content with the results from his *Trieste* voyage. In 1964–65 he was back, again chasing the scattering layer. This time he was aboard the Westinghouse-Cousteau diving saucer, the little submarine that takes two men to a depth of 1,000 feet.

On one of her dives off Mexico, the saucer hovered where the scattering layer was, as shown by an echo sounder on the surface boat. The saucer's lights were repeatedly switched on for two minuates and off for three. There were jellyfish. There were lantern fish —bathypelagic fish with luminous organs, or photophores, in specific patterns. Barham and his pilot followed the scattering layer down. They saw euphausid shrimp, prawn, then hundreds of lantern fish. The surface boat with them detected some large scattering organisms, maybe big animals, but the men in the diving saucer saw none. On a night dive Barham and Canoe Kientzy saw lantern fish; they were the most important part of the scattering layer, apparently, as observed from the diving saucer off Mexico.

That situation changed when the saucer returned to California. Off Point Loma, Barham saw a number of siphonophores that coincided with the layer. He felt, as he had after his experience aboard the *Trieste,* that the siphonophores were the main part of the deep 900-foot scattering layer off southern California.

In 1963 in the Red Sea, Britain's brand-new research ship *Dis-*

covery encountered the scattering layer. "There was evidence of small fish causing scattering layers," Dr. G. E. R. Deacon, Director of the National Institute of Oceanography at Wormley, Sussex, England, reported, "and numerous dense echoes from what appeared to be moderate-sized fish at about 250 meters. It will take a long time to analyze these records."

At Woods Hole late in 1964 I talked with Richard H. Backus, a marine biologist who is also an associate in ichthyology at Harvard University, and who has been studying the scattering layer at sea. He has used a complex, multi-frequency sound rather than a single-frequency device such as the echo sounder. "Typically," he says, "these layers move up toward the surface at night. With the setting of the sun, they start up rapidly; with dawn, they start down rapidly. You find, for example, that when the depth changes, the frequency of the sound scattered by the organisms changes. The closer they are to the surface, the lower the frequency of the scattered sound. By studying this relationship, you can say that the effective sound scatterer is a bubble, a bubble of gas. To be a good sound scatterer it must be different—less dense and more compressible than seawater. In short, you look for a marine animal that carries this bubble of gas." Dr. Backus seeks a gas-filled swim bladder, or air bladder, that matches his acoustical results.

Dr. Backus says some siphonophores have such a bubble and would be good sound scatterers. Little, he says, is known of the geographical and vertical distribution of siphonophores. He finds the lantern fish, which Dr. Barham also spotted, to be qualified as sound scatterers. They have gas-filled bladders. He finds euphausid shrimps scatter some of the sound but, because they lack the bubble of gas, they must be accounted only weak scatterers. These shrimps, about half an inch long, are transparent. Their interior organs show through. Most are colorless. Some are pink, scarlet, and pale green. "The eyes," said William Beebe, "stood out as of burnished jet." When Beebe photographed them, they tried to stay away from the light. Euphausids themselves glow. Six of them, in a glass jar, can radiate light enough for a man to read a newspaper by. There are many species of euphausids, which are also called krill, and are important in the diet of the humpbacked whale, the fin whale, and the blue, or sulphur-bottom whale, the biggest (to 150 tons) animal that ever has lived. But the shrimp are such weak scatterers, they would not return echoes as strong as those returned by the deep scattering layers. The layers appear denser than the most dense concentrations of shrimps ever known. Furthermore, euphausids are greatly concentrated in the Antarctic, where the deep scattering layer is not found. What about squid? Some cephalopods —squid, octopus, spirula, pearly nautilus—enclose the necessary gas bubbles. Most don't. Dr. Backus stresses that we do not know as much about the distribution of these animals as we would like to. "In every layer we've studied," he says, "about six, in the Atlantic and Mediterranean, the gas bubbles are always involved."

Near the surface of the ocean, he says, there is a whole host of layered sound-scattering phenomena. "There are also things coming up from intermediate depths, from great depths, from shallow depths. Most changes result in the animals getting nearer the surface at night." But there are also movements in the other direction: "Some—they are unusual—go deeper at night." The upward migration, Dr. Backus believes, is mainly in order to secure food. Then why do the animals not stay at the surface? Perhaps it's safer—less predation—at deeper levels in the daytime. "What of the one out of a hundred animals that reverses the procedure and goes deeper at night?" Dr. Backus asks himself, and answers, "I've no idea." Other unanswered questions are: Are there two or three favorite patterns of distribution in the Atlantic scattering layer? How many animals are in it? Several hundred species of fishes are involved, Dr. Backus believes. "No fish is ever found everywhere in the North Atlantic." The lantern fish could be a big part of the layer: "As a family, lantern fishes are everywhere, but no individual species is in found from North Greenland to the equator; but the scattering layer is both places." What physical or chemical factors control the layer? How did the patterns of the layer come to exist? In short, the deep scattering layer (or layers), discovered during World War II and brought to wide notice since, is still a mystery. The first eyewitnesses have reached it but have brought back only fragmentary results. More trips to the depths must be made to solve what has become a great riddle of the seas.

Is There a Missing Link
in the Food Chain?

ONE OF THE BIGGEST MYSTERIES of the ocean may be on its way to being solved. It is a mystery that has been oceanwide. The answer, until now, has been hidden in the depths of the sea.

This mystery can be put very simply: What do they eat? Or, to put it another way: What basic food supports all life in the sea?

You know the traditional explanation: Big fish eat smaller fish. Smaller fish eat still littler fish. And so on, till you reach the tiniest animals of all. These are the zooplankton. Some are one-celled; many can be seen only with a microscope; most are not more than a fraction of an inch long; and they live by billions upon billions upon billions in the sea. There are many different kinds of animals in the zooplankton; small crustacea are quantitatively the most important.

The tiniest of the tiny zooplankton have been supposed to live by consuming the tiniest plants in the sea. The zooplankton, in other words, have been considered plant-eaters, as are cows and rabbits on land. That has been the belief.

But there have been difficulties with the theory. Are there enough phytoplankton (plants) in the sea to support the zooplankton (animals)? Many scientists have thought not.

Are phytoplankton always on hand to provide food for the zooplankton? Not necessarily. Phytoplankton, like other plants, need sunlight. They thrive therefore near the surface of the sea.

Zooplankton are found in the depths as well as near the surface. What do the deep-dwelling zooplankton—these minute animals of the dark waters—live on? Even if some tiny plants are found in the depths, are there enough?

Animals—even the tiniest ones like zooplankton—must have something to eat. If there are not enough infinitesimal plants on hand, what do the zooplankton eat? Each other? Yes, in some instances, but not all.

What about the wintertime at sea? There certainly does not appear to be enough phytoplankton in the winter to sustain animal life in the sea until the next spring. There are the four seasons in the sea, as on land. The phytoplankton, during the dark months of winter—just like plants on land—die or lie dormant.

So there seems to be something missing from man's knowledge of food for the tiniest sea animals, the zooplankton.

Could there just possibly be a food supply in the mysterious "Milky Way" or "living soup" that Jacques-Yves Cousteau saw beneath the sea? Divers and men in bathyscaphes also frequently have reported seeing something like "snowfalls" going on in the depths of the sea. Could this be the food supply for the tiniest animals in the ocean?

The answer, it turns out, is quite probably Yes. What these explorers saw may be much more important than they thought.

Three American scientists now have an idea what these snowfalls or Milky Ways are. They think they may provide food for the zooplankton.

If so, it is a new kind of food not known to exist before. And if it is a supply of food for marine life, it may well be a vast food supply—a far greater amount of nutriment—than anyone thought the zooplankton had available.

The scientists believe that they have found a new bread basket for the uncountable billions of zooplankton. They are Dr. Gordon Riley, formerly of Yale University and now Director of the Institute of Oceanography at Dalhousie University, Halifax, Nova

Scotia, Canada; Dr. E. R. Baylor of the Woods Hole Oceanographic Institution, and Dr. W. H. Sutcliffe of Lehigh University, who worked at Woods Hole. Their research was conducted under grants from the National Science Foundation.

In suggesting the new food supply and how it comes into existence, the three scientists propose a completely new idea about what goes on in the depths of the ocean.

Science long has known that there are in the ocean huge quantities of once-living matter both dissolved in the water and in the form of tiny particles. There is in the sea, it is estimated, at least 50 times as much of this nonliving matter as there are living plants and animals. These nonliving particles are composed of dead plants and animals and of material secreted by plants and animals.

This dissolved matter was believed to be in forms the living animals could not use, i.e., could not eat.

But possibly the nonliving matter could be made edible. In a laboratory at Woods Hole, Dr. Baylor and Dr. Sutcliffe discovered that this nonliving matter in the sea could be reconstituted, or changed back, into particles that are immediately suitable for zooplankton food.

How?

It happens, Dr. Baylor and Dr. Sutcliffe learned, when the nonliving matter adheres to air bubbles in the water. Continued bubbling of the water results in the building up of larger and larger clumps of particles.

The bubbling takes place in the top 300 feet of water. High pressure prevents bubbles at greater depths. But the food formed can sink into deep water and can adsorb other organic matter on the way down. And very small particles can agglutinate to form larger particles, and more food in deep water.

Dr. Riley, Dr. Baylor, and Dr. Sutcliffe today believe that food particles for the tiniest sea animals, including the zooplankton, are continually being created in the ocean by this process of adsorption (sticking) to air bubbles and to other particles.

Tiny blobs of material on air bubbles, which the zooplankton can eat, Dr. Riley believes, make up the mysterious living soup reported by eyewitnesses to occur in the depths.

This food from nonliving matter is continually being replenished. Dead and decaying organisms, plants, and animals, continually increase the nonliving matter in the ocean. The other source of nonliving matter, secretions from phytoplankton and zooplankton, also continually increases the amount on hand.

A good portion of the remains of plants and animals is eaten as it sinks through the depths. There is still a great supply of nonliving food in the sea. It decreases with depth in about the first 1,500 feet of the ocean. Below this depth, the amount of it remains steady, because more of it is constantly being created by the adhesion of particles to other particles in the water. This is, Dr. Riley thinks, the main food supply of deepwater zooplankton.

What causes the bubbles, and thus builds the food supply?

Dr. Riley, who worked in Long Island Sound and who used water samples from widely scattered parts of the Atlantic, thinks that the action of waves creates some bubbles at all seasons, and that, especially in winter, storms create bubbles.

If the food supply of the depths is brought into being by storms, it also means that the life of men and animals who eat fish and otherwise are supported by the sea is at least partly dependent for its existence on typhoons of the Pacific, hurricanes of the Atlantic, and the great gales around the Antarctic, where the belts of strong winds are called the Roaring Forties, the Howling Fifties, and the Screaming Sixties. A winter storm may supply food for zooplankton when there is little else to eat, and thus the storm would support the first link in the food chain for animal life in the sea.

The zooplankton, Dr. Riley says, have a distinct pattern of vertical migration (up and down like the mysterious deep scattering layer, of which they may be a part). This up-and-down movement, he says, ensures that the zooplankton get within reach of available food (tiny plants, or phytoplankton, on the surface, air-bubble dinners far beneath the surface).

A marine biologist at Dalhousie University, Dr. P. J. Wangersky, decided to see if he could create some of the nonliving food matter on his own. So he bubbled a mixture of artificial seawater. He found that, indeed, the particles could be concentrated on bubbles and thus they could be made to form blobs or molecules of non-living food.

Dr. Wangersky believes, the National Science Foundation reported, that this mechanism of adsorption to bubbles may have been one important step in a long process that led from inorganic chemicals to the development of life in the sea. These aggregates formed on air bubbles might be the progenitors of all life, including man.

"Even if life did not trace its ancestry back to air bubbles in the sea," Dr. Riley has said, "it seems certain that if a stable marine food supply created from a vast reservoir of dissolved organic matter did not exist, there would be less life today and fewer stable forms. Probably most deep-sea life would be nonexistent since organic particulate matter appears to be their basic food source."

The work of Dr. Riley and his associates has led to the concept of a new base for the food chain in the sea. There are at present a thousand unanswered questions about the air bubbles that all the life in the sea may depend on. The research is continuing.

What Will the Mohole Reveal?

FOR THE MEN directing the work on Project Mohole, the biggest question is: "What is the earth made of?" They hope to find the answer beneath the bottom of the sea.

To find the answer—if they do—they will first have to accomplish one of the most difficult tasks ever attempted at sea.

They will have to drill down for the first time through 2½ to 3 miles of open sea, down through water constantly in motion, down through the sediment on the ocean floor, down for the first time through the crust of the earth itself; down for the first time through the boundary between the earth's crust and the mantle— the so-called Mohorovicic discontinuity, or Moho, for which the project is named; and down into the very mantle of the earth itself.

If their drill grinds into the mantle, six to seven miles beneath the sea's surface, almost three miles beneath the sea's floor, men will have penetrated the mantle for the first time. Here in the mantle scientists should obtain the answer to their age-old question, the most important unanswered question in the science of geophysics, "What is the earth made of?" For the mantle is itself 84 percent of the globe. It extends 1,800 miles, or almost halfway, of the nearly 4,000 miles to the center of the earth. The mantle is, scientists believe, hot, viscous, black rock. But the behavior of the mantle is mysterious and puzzling even to scientists who know most about it. Its appearance is a matter of conjecture. As Lord Kelvin pointed out, when the mantle is subjected to sudden forces, it responds as though it were made of steel—an earthquake causes the earth to "ring like a bell." At other times, the mantle acts like a soft plastic.

Far inside the mantle, those 1,800 miles inside, far out of reach of man, there begins the earth's core, probably an outer layer of molten iron around a center (under unimaginable pressure) of solid iron, 1,800 miles in diameter, at the very heart of the globe. The liquid and solid cores have been postulated to explain the weight of the earth and variations in speed with which seismic, or earthquake waves, travel through different substances.

Once the men of the Mohole have obtained samples of the rock that composes the mantle and therefore composes most of the earth, they will be on their way to answering other questions: What was the origin of the earth? Is the rock of the mantle the same as the rock of meteorites, as some suppose? If so, is this evidence that the other planets, the moon, and the earth were all fragments torn off the sun, hurled into space, and hardened into solid rock as they cooled?

Or is there instead, as some scientists think more likely, evidence in the composition of the mantle that earth and sun and planets were formed by the condensation of clouds of dust and gas similar to the clouds that today are scattered, it is believed, throughout the universe? How old is the earth? Either in the mantle itself, or above the mantle deep inside the earth's crust, there should be found rocks far older than any other rocks ever obtained on land (our oldest rocks so far date back 600 million years) or dredged up from the bottom of the sea (100 million years). If samples of such ancient rocks can be obtained, the National Science Foundation points out, a direct and more accurate age for the earth can be determined by studying the radioactivity of the minerals within the rocks. Estimates of the earth's age today, by many scientists, are around 4.55 billion years, or the figure that the Carnegie Institution and the U.S. Geological Survey recently came up with, 4.7 billion years.

How old are the oceans, and how did they become filled with water? Says the National Science Foundation's *Project Mohole,*

> It was once believed that the oceans were filled by torrential, centuries-long rains. However, most scientists now accept the theory that water trapped in the earth's interior, from the time of its formation, has gradually worked its way outward and filled the ocean basins.
>
> Some oceanographers believe that most of this water, largely in the form of volcanic steam, was added when the earth was young. They believe that the oceans have for the past 2 billion years or so been much the same as they are today, and that the amount of water added during the last 500 million years is insignificant. Others believe that water has been seeping out at the same rate since the formation of the earth, some 4½ billion years ago. They calculate that the present rate of seepage from volcanoes, deep cracks, and hot springs is more than enough to account for all the water in the oceans, if it is assumed that the rate has been constant for billions of years. Still other scientists believe that a vast and far-reaching change took place in the earth's crust between 60 to 100 million years ago and that as much as 25 percent of the water was added to the oceans at that time.
>
> When widely distributed samples of the lowest layers of sediment and the underlying rock are obtained from both the Pacific and Atlantic basins, they should help scientists decide which of these theories is correct.

Is the earth getting hotter or colder? Are its ice caps and glaciers shrinking or spreading? Is the sea itself receding or rising? What causes the heat of the earth? The formation of the earth? If so, the earth must be cooling. Or is it caused by radioactive decay deep in the earth's interior? If so, the earth may be getting hotter.

How did life on earth begin? On the way down to the earth's

crust, in the sediment and mud on the ocean bottom, the drill of the Mohole may encounter, and will sample, the buried fossils of early life forms. How old will they be? Some scientists believe life on earth is 2 or 3 billion years old. The oldest fossil found on land (neopilina, a tiny snail-like creature that today still lives in the sediment on the sea floor) is only 500 million years old. The Mohole drill will take us back through hundreds of millions of years of the history of life as well as of the history of the earth itself.

The Mohole tentatively will be drilled about 170 miles north-northeast of Honolulu, near Molokai and Maui, both Hawaiian islands. The proposed site is at lat. 22° 22′ N. and long. 155° 28′ W.

The plan is to drill Mohole at sea because beneath the ocean the earth's crust is far thinner than it is on land. On land the crust averages 20 miles in thickness, while at sea it thins down to about three miles and, therefore, can be penetrated. The Hawaii site was selected as a compromise. It appeared the best of several possible sites. Others were considered near Puerto Rico and the Caribbean island of Antigua, but they were in hurricane belts and seemed to have other shortcomings. The site near Maui is not in a typhoon area, it is near large harbor and dock facilities, and the distance down to the mantle is not too great.

The Pacific is 14,000 feet deep at the Mohole site, and the estimated total distance to the mantle lies between 28,000 and 33,000 feet. It is not believed practical at this time to attempt to drill beyond a total distance of 35,000 feet, or almost 7 miles. The deepest well man has drilled on dry land is slightly less than 5 miles, or 25,340 feet. This well, in western Texas, required two years and 20 days to complete; and half of this time was spent in inching down the last 6,000 feet. The well produced neither oil nor gas.

Men themselves have penetrated the solid earth to a depth of two miles in the mines of South Africa, where they mine diamonds with the help of a half-million-dollar air-conditioning plant. Every

1,000 feet down, the National Geographic Society says, the temperature rises approximately 15 degrees Fahrenheit.

Mohole started as a joke.

Back in 1952 a few of the nation's leading scientists banded themselves together in what they called AMSOC: The American Miscellaneous Society. It was "miscellaneous" as a gibe at scientific societies that sometimes get too specialized for their own good.

AMSOC had no bylaws, officers, publications, or formal members. Some of its meetings (with two considered a quorum) took place at cocktail time in Washington, D.C. AMSOC's first close ties were with the Committee for Informing Animals of Their Taxonomic Position and the Committee for Cooperation with Visitors from Outer Space.

One day AMSOC had a breakfast (I believe this was at or near the Scripps Institution of Oceanography in San Diego, California) and the conversation about deep-drilling projects became serious. Five Amsockers were members of the National Academy of Sciences, which presently took over the idea and AMSOC with it. And AMSOC had to organize itself formally to receive funds for the project.

The Amsockers who started it all were Gordon Lill, then of the Office of Naval Research, and today the National Science Foundation's director of the entire Mohole project; Dr. William Heroy, a geologist; Dr. Harry Ladd, a paleontologist; Dr. Arthur Maxwell, a geophysicist of the Office of Naval Research; Professor Roger Revelle, geophysicist, then director of the Scripps Institution of Oceanography; Professor Walter Munk, geophysicist, of the Scripps Institution; Dr. William Rubey, U.S. Geological Survey; Dr. Joshua Tracey, geologist; Willard Bascom, today president of an ocean engineering company in Washington, D.C.; Maurice Ewing, Columbia University's ocean explorer; and Dr. Harry Hess, professor in the Department of Geology at Princeton University. Hess, a naval officer in World War II, had become, with the help of his echo-sounding apparatus, the discoverer of the Cape Johnson Deep, and of guyots. (Guyots are flat-topped mountains beneath the seas, which are believed to be drowned islands that sank too fast for coral reefs to grow on top of them. Guyots were named after a nineteenth-century Princeton professor of geology, Arnold Guyot.)

The original Amsockers had asked themselves what they knew was a wild question, What project would yield the most information about the earth? They dreamed up Mohole as the answer for reasons already given. The Mohole project, the Amsockers knew, was a pipedream, pie-in-the-sky, unattainable, a castle in the air. The whole idea might have died right there. That it didn't is a tribute to its importance. Back in the 1930's Dr. T. A. Jagger of Hawaiian Volcano Observatory proposed drilling 1,000 holes in various ocean basins, each 1,000 feet deep, so geology of suboceanic regions "would not rest on speculation alone." One of the first published suggestions for drilling through the crust and into the mantle was made by Dr. Frank Estabrook in 1956. A sample of the mantle, the material that comprises over five-sixths of our earth, says Thomas Wallace Donnelly of the geology department at Rice University, Houston, "will be for the earth sciences what the smashing of the atom has been for physics."

The original Amsockers were correct in thinking that Mohole was impossible; until recently, it was. It is only barely possible today, and is barely possible because of the development of, and man's experience with, new tools. One new tool that makes Mohole possible is the computer. Mohole will be drilled from a floating platform over the Hawaii drill site. The water is far too deep for the platform to be anchored. But the unanchored platform must not move over 850 feet from its exact spot in midocean. It will have no landmarks in sight to go by. So it will be kept in exact position by the problem-solving of a computer. The electronic brain will receive information from radar, sonar, and other sources, will do its figuring, and will automatically control the six 750-horsepower outboard motors spaced around the drilling platform so that they keep the platform where it ought to be. The Honeywell Corporation and General Motors Research designed the controls.

Another computer has already worked on Mohole: it has tested the drilling platform. And since the drilling platform has not even been constructed yet, this would have presented a nice problem before we had computers. Late in 1963 at Schenectady, New York, the General Electric Company began a computer program to predict the effects of winds up to 160 miles an hour, with gusts of 250, and of waves and currents on the platform. The computer took into consideration heave, pitch, roll, sway, yaw, and surge. The whole business was so complicated that no computer ordinarily could solve such problems, so GE had to work out a new system for the computer to use. At the end GE could explain, using the only possible language, mathematics, the movements that the platform would make and the forces that would cause these movements in all directions. After GE's electronic brain got through, models of the platform were built and tested further at the Navy's David Taylor Model Basin and at other model basins at the University of Michigan and the Stevens Institute of Technology.

The prime contractor—the company charged with drilling Mohole—is Brown & Root, Inc., of Houston, one of the nation's heavy construction firms. Brown & Root, among other things, built 500 naval vessels during World War II and designed the Manned Spacecraft Center in Houston. It is known as a fly-by-night outfit—its engineers fly all night to start work at 7 A.M. The company's nickname is "Root and Scoot." Brown & Root as long ago as 1956 drilled for oil from floating vessels in the Gulf of Mexico and off the coast of Maine. The company has engaged in the search for petroleum offshore in the Gulf of Mexico, the Atlantic, the Mediterranean, and the Persian Gulf. For help on designing the Mohole drilling platform Brown & Root called in Gibbs and Cox, Inc., a New York marine architectural firm which, among other things, designed the *United States,* the streamlined, largely aluminum, blue-ribbon holder of the Atlantic speed record for passenger liners.

From designs by the Mohole staff, Gibbs and Cox prepared plans and specifications for a drilling platform like no drilling platform ever built before. It is, of course, the largest ever proposed. It is called "the floating acre." Its size compares with that of a football field: 280 feet long, 235 feet wide. It is 135 feet high from twin keels to upper deck. Its derrick is 240 feet high. It is also, as is necessary for the Mohole project, the most sophisticated drilling platform ever proposed. It will float over the Hawaii hole in the bottom of the sea on two submerged, submarinelike hulls, each 35 feet in diameter and 390 feet long, or considerably longer than many of our submarines and more nearly the length of a freighter. Main engines will drive the platform to the Mohole location at 8 to 10 knots. Propellers are at the rear of each hull.

It may take, scientists estimate, three years to drill through the earth's crust into the mantle. The platform must keep the top of the long string of steel pipe reaching down to the drill in position all that time.

A platform rather than a ship was decided upon to drill Mohole partly because of progress made with platforms in drilling offshore oil wells at sea. These platforms have produced remarkable records. In 1963 in the Gulf of Mexico one platform shut down for only 7 days because of the weather, although there were 79 days when wave heights ranged from 10 to 29 feet. The roll (side-to-side movement) and the pitch (rise and fall of bow and stern) of the platform exceeded 2 degrees only when height of the waves exceeded 20 feet. Another offshore platform measured less than 10 inches of heave (rise and fall of the entire vessel) when the waves were estimated above 25 feet and winds above 80 miles an hour.

Living quarters, laboratories, all machinery, and drilling equipment will be in or upon the upper deck of the Mohole platform. The lower hulls beneath the surface will hold fuel, ballast, and drilling mud (used to remove the cuttings from the hole as the bit chews through the rock beneath the sea). The drilling derrick itself will be at the very center of the upper deck, the position of minimum deck movement.

Nevertheless, a thousand problems will beset the Mohole men. How can the hole be drilled? "In order to understand the difficulties involved," says Rice University's Dr. Donnelly, "imagine yourself in a small, pitching helicopter hovering at about the level of the upper floor of the Shamrock-Hilton" (an 18-story hotel in Houston). "Lower a thin wire (about $\frac{1}{16}$-inch) with a small drill bit at the end from the helicopter and try to drill a hole in the concrete to a depth nearly equal to the height of the helicopter." Sometimes you have to haul the drill to the surface for inspection. How do you get the drill back into the hole? The actual size of the hole will be about 10 inches in diameter.

How do you keep the enormous weight of the drill pipe itself—35,000 feet, or almost 7 miles, of it—from being so heavy (it will weigh as much as three-quarters of a million pounds) that it will pull itself apart? What will changing ocean currents do as they exert force on the 2½-mile-long string of drill pipe extending through the seawater itself? Are there tools rugged enough to do the job?

There may be. At the Leona Valley Ranch, near Uvalde, Texas, a new motor recently drove a corer through dense basaltic rock believed to be like the rock beneath the bottom of the sea. This rock is the toughest medium yet found for testing Mohole tools. The bits, encrusted with diamonds, the hardest substance known to man, lasted while drilling the rock far longer than expected. The turbo-corer was developed by two years' joint work by the Mohole staff and Dresser Industries, Inc. Field Drilling Company of San Antonio, Texas, drilled the hole in the basaltic rock.

In 1960 the first test holes at sea for the Mohole project were drilled, as a study of Mohole's feasibility. Drilling was from a barge, *CUSS I*—owned originally by the Continental, Union, Superior and Shell oil companies, and operated by the Global Marine Exploration Co.

The *CUSS I* was hauled to a site off Guadalupe Island, Mexico, 220 miles south of San Diego. Here, through 11,700 feet of water, five holes were drilled, the deepest 601 feet. C. Don Woodson of Texaco, Inc., was drilling superintendent; Willard Bascom was field director.

Sediment corings the *CUSS I* brought up showed fossil evidence, the National Science Foundation says, "of an extensive sea life of Late to Middle Miocene age (15 to 20 million years ago) in the Guadalupe Island area. More than 500 feet of nearly continuous core of the deep ocean ooze showed that, compared with the amount of life of the earlier period, the area today is an oceanic wasteland."

Two of the holes at the Guadalupe site for the first time in history penetrated the second layer of the earth's crust. They showed that at least the top of the second layer near Guadalupe was basalt, a hard rock formed by the solidification of lava.

In November, 1962, a 1,000-foot-long core was obtained from still another site, on the west coast of Puerto Rico. This core was of serpentine—a rock that may be present under the ocean in the deeper part of the earth's crust.

Then came the selection of the site near Maui, in the State of Hawaii, for the eventual drilling of Mohole itself. The original members of the Committee of the National Academy of Sciences—National Science Foundation who picked out the site were Dr. Harry H. Hess of Princeton, chairman; Dr. Brackett Hersey, Woods Hole; Dr. Jack Nafe, Lamont Geological Observatory, Columbia University; and Dr. Russell Raitt and Dr. George Shor, both of Scripps. In May, 1964, the National Academy of Sciences reconstituted the committee to a three-member panel: Dr. Hess, Dr. Hersey, and Dr. Shor. Alternate members are Dr. Raitt and Dr. John Ewing of Lamont Geological Observatory. Taking part in geophysical surveys at sea to help find a site were Woods Hole, Lamont, Texas A. & M. University, Scripps, and these companies: Western Geophysical, Inc., Los Angeles, California; The Offshore Exploration Group, Inc., Houston; Brown & Root, Inc., Houston;

and Decca, Inc., of New York City. The head of the National
Science Foundation's Mole Project office is Daniel Hunt, Jr., a
former Navy captain.

Besides the Mohole itself, other holes will be drilled in the
Pacific, principally to study sediments and the records of life and
earth history in them. These will be northwest of San Francisco at
the Mendocino Scarp; west of Seattle, Washington, and east of the
Cobb Seamount; in the Cascadia Abyssal Plain west of Seattle; in
the San Diego Trough, off the coast between Los Angeles and
San Diego; in the Cocos Ridge area, southwest of Panama; and
both north and south of Maui, Hawaii.

The American public has been wondering about the center of
the earth at least since the nineteenth century. In the 1800's many
Americans believed the globe to be hollow. Bills were introduced
in Congress proposing that a Navy expedition sail into the inside
of the earth; there was supposed to be an entrance hole somewhere
in the Antarctic.

Objections to the Mohole project have been raised, as you might
expect. In 1965, Frank Carey of the Associated Press reported
some of those on the minds of some citizens:

> ... If you bore a deep hole in the ocean bottom, all
> the water is going to run out, as it does when you pull
> the plug in the bathtub.
> ... If the inside of the earth is hot, the water running
> in is going to generate a lot of steam that will blow up
> the planet.
> ... Below the crust, the earth is hollow—a great big
> vacuum chamber—so when you punch a hole into this
> vacuum, the earth is going to "implode," that is, explode
> inward.
> ... Hell's down there, mister, so when you dig that
> hole you're gonna loose the fires, to say nothing of all
> those devils.

Scientists think that these objections are not valid. Besides telling us what the globe is made of, and something of the history of life, they expect Mohole to unravel other secrets, at least partly: how earthquakes begin; how volcanic eruptions occur; what the surface of the moon is like—some think when we reach the earth's mantle we will have reached something much like the moon. We also want to know whether there is oil and natural gas beneath deeper water (the Mohole itself is not expected to strike oil) and how to explore for it.

How to do heavy work far beneath the sea is by itself knowledge worth having as men explore the depths, and the Mohole should provide plenty of evidence. All of these things, scientists feel, offset any objections to drilling the Mohole.

There is, however, one objection that might prove valid. Maybe it isn't necessary to find out about the earth's mantle, to drill Mohole at all. Maybe we do know what the mantle is made of. Maybe we have been looking at it right along. What about meteorites? Are they the same as the mantle? What about rocks spewed out by volcanoes—volcanoes reach far inside the earth? What about the previously unknown rock, iron-heavy black and green stones, that Russians in 1966 announced they had collected with a toothed steel drag in the Indian Ocean? The Russians believe it is rock from the upper mantle thrust up through the deep rifts found in the midocean ridges that girdle the globe.

There is, furthermore, a chance that St. Peter and St. Paul's Rocks, those bleak islands in the Atlantic near the equator where the nuclear submarine *Triton* began and ended her round-the-world trip, are composed of material thrust up out of the mantle. Their structure, says *Sea Frontiers,* is unlike that of any other Atlantic islands. There is some evidence that they are a sample of the earth's mantle, right out in the open, where it can be seen at anytime, and without drilling almost 7 miles beneath the sea surface. But we are not sure. It is hard to tell how we can be sure until the Mohole is drilled.

What Are the Secrets
of the Coelacanth?

G. F. CARTWRIGHT came upon the large, strange fish when he was skin diving. His experience is an example of the value of eye-witnesses beneath the sea. He was not looking for anything unique. Late in 1952 he was simply roving around beneath the surface of the ocean at Malindi, off the east coast of Africa near the Comoro Islands.

What Mr. Cartwright saw was astonishing. The big fish, he said afterward, "looked wholly evil and a thousand years old. It had a large eye and the most outstanding feature was the armor-plate effect of its heavy scales. . . ."

What Mr. Cartwright was staring at, in the shadowy waters near eastern Africa, may have been the fish that was to be known as the greatest natural-history discovery of the twentieth century: the coelacanth. That the greatest find of recent years should come from beneath the surface—coelacanths are believed today to live from 500 to 1,000 feet down—should not, perhaps, be surprising. The opaqueness of the sea hides the animals that dwell in it. For many marine biologists, the question of sea exploration is, What animals are down there? No one knows them all. Men keep finding new marine animals all the time. They even find big ones: coelacanths have been caught up to 6 feet long and 150 pounds in weight.

The coelacanth had actually already been discovered once, accidentally, before Mr. Cartwright's skin-diving adventure. Its discovery was an example of how sometimes amateur scientists rather than professionals—in this case, fishermen—can contribute new knowledge to marine science. There are, for example, 1,500 shoreline, fish-watching skin divers in the American Littoral Society, an organization encouraged by the Marine Laboratory of the Bureau of Sport Fisheries and Wildlife at Sandy Hook, N.J., who let the laboratory know of any unusual experiences they have, or of any peculiar fish or animals they see, and also report on conditions they find in the water. Lionel Walford, the head of the Sandy Hook laboratory and one of the United States' great experts on life in the sea, will tell you that there is still too much to be learned about the sea and the life in it to leave it to scientists alone.

The very first coelacanth was captured purely by chance. Men had known for a long time what a coelacanth was. It was a prehistoric fish. It lived 250 million years ago, along with dinosaurs. We have its fossils. Many were dug up when the excavations were made for the library at Princeton University. They have been found in other places as well. To judge from its fossils, the coelacanth died out around 70 million years ago. No more recent fossils of the fish have been located. It was a primitive fish. Its fins—almost like arms—could tell us something about how arms developed during eons of time. But no scientist, before 1938, thought a live coelacanth would ever again be seen.

Then just before Christmas 1938, a trawler was out in the Indian Ocean off East London, South Africa, looking for a place to drop her trawl. Her skipper, Captain Goosen, decided to have a run on the bank near the mouth of the Chalumi River. This is not a good trawling area, but sometimes fishermen do have luck here. Captain Goosen dropped his net three miles offshore, to about 240 feet deep. He was trawling the inshore section of a shelf about 10 miles wide, running to its seaward edge at about 360 feet deep—the continental slope, where the bottom plunges toward the deep sea.

The trawl came up. The fishermen had had fair luck. They had about a ton and a half of edible fish, not of the highest grade, but edible, nevertheless. There were also several tons of shark.

There was also—fortunately it had not been crushed by the sharks or other fish—a large blue fish with big scales. It looked like none of the others. None of the fishermen had seen anything like it. They called Captain Goosen. He looked at it, touched its body. It heaved itself up and snapped its jaws viciously. It almost caught his hand. Its mouth, Captain Goosen noted, was lined with fangs.

Captain Goosen headed his trawler for East London. He radioed Miss M. Courtenay-Latimer of the local museum that he was coming in and was bringing a haul of fish for her to examine. This was not unusual. As a local scientist, she regularly inspected Captain Goosen's catch.

She saw the ordinary fish and the sharks. Then her eye fell on the large blue fish with the big scales. She had it pulled out. She had seen nothing like it before. She asked an old trawlerman if he had; not in 30 years, he replied. He pointed out that the fins were like arms, that the fish almost looked like a big lizard. The fish was 5 feet long and weighed 127 pounds. The day was hot; this fish smelled even worse than most fish.

Miss Courtenay-Latimer sent a sketch of the fish on to James Leonard Brierley Smith, an ichthyologist at Rhodes University, Grahamstown, South Africa.

Smith got the sketch in the mail just after New Year's Day, 1939. He stared at it. "I told myself sternly not to be a fool," he says, "but there was something about that sketch that seized on my imagination and told me that this was something very far beyond the usual run of fishes in our seas. It was as if my common sense were waging a battle with my perception . . . I kept on staring at that sketch."

He pondered the big scales. He pondered the limblike fins. "Large, blue-enameled scales and lobed fins, attached by 'stalks' to the long body, are characteristic of the coelacanth," says F. D.

Ommanney in *The Fishes*. "No other fish," Ommanney goes on, "has or has ever had such a tail pattern."

Smith noticed the broad, flat tail, with a fanlike tuft at the end. He comments: "One alone in a sketch might be passed; but all together! At the same time what I suspected was so utterly preposterous that my common sense kept up a steady fire of scorn for my idiocy in even thinking of it." What Dr. Smith thought, of course, was that the sketch looked like a coelacanth; as a fish scientist, he knew, of course, that the coelacanth had died out 70 million years before. But here was the drawing. "Right up to 1938," says Dr. Smith, "no scientist had ever seen or even suspected the existence of a living coelacanth."

Dr. Smith met several people who thought they had seen fish something like the one in the drawing. One man remembered seeing one washed up on the shore near East London. Dr. Smith decided to pursue the matter, that is, to pursue the coelacanth. He had a circular printed with a picture of the coelacanth, and he offered a reward of one hundred pounds ($280). The drawing on the circular showed the big fins and caused the crews of trawlers to give the coelacanth a nickname it still carries: Old Fourlegs.

But for years no coelacanth turned up.

Dr. Smith thought one might. "Nowhere in all the temperate and tropical oceans was there at that time so great an area whose marine fauna had been so little investigated and which was so little known as East Africa. The whole area is full of reefs, rocky and coral reefs, some enormous, many hardly known. Add to this that the set of the current from north of Madagascar is always southwards. I could see no reason why the coelacanth should not live normally in some remote and probably uncivilized part of that vast area. As I surveyed all the facts and evidence, it seemed very likely. This one, caught near East London, could easily have come rambling down the coast in the warm Mozambique Current, as quite a number of tropical fishes constantly do." But the years went by and no coelacanth appeared.

Dr. Smith solved another problem: "It had been my good fortune," he writes in *The Search Beneath the Sea,* "to solve the mystery of the identity of a strange fish, a man-size parrot fish which was only occasionally seen. It was a curious creature with a big hump on its head, but at that time its scientific identity was unknown. I hunted for this creature continually and offered a reward for one, but in vain, until . . . I spotted over 200 of these peculiar large fishes in a deep channel off Pungutiach island (South Kenya) and by means of considerable exertions managed to capture no less than eight of them, the largest weighing over 130 pounds."

In September 1952, Smith and his wife were working in Zanzibar. A friend of his wife's brought along, and introduced to them, a man named Eric Hunt. Hunt did some commercial fishing, and Smith gave him some of his pamphlets about the coelacanth. Hunt, who traded with the Comoro Islands, took the pamphlets back with him on his schooner, and distributed them far and wide to the natives of the Comoros.

It was almost exactly 14 years after the first coelacanth had been trawled up, when the second one was taken. Ahmed Hussein of Domoni, a village on the coast of Anjouan, one of the Comoro Islands, on December 20, 1952, let down his long line into about 120 feet of water. Hussein caught a large fish. It fought. He battered its head. Next morning a teacher saw the fish at the local market. The teacher, who had read the leaflet, urged Hussein to take the fish to Hunt. So the 90-pound fish was toted, in blazing heat, 25 miles across mountainous country to Eric Hunt. The fish was putrefying. But Hunt recognized it instantly and sent a cable to Dr. Smith. It arrived Christmas Eve, 1952:

HAVE FIVE FOOT SPECIMEN COELACANTH INJECTED FORMALIN HERE KILLED 20TH ADVISE REPLY HUNT.

Smith was in Durban, South Africa, when he got the cable. "Everything with coelacanths so far had been troublesome," he recalls, "and here was quite the worst situation I had ever encountered. . . . This precious fish was so far away, in one of the worst places in the world for safe preservation with probably only a mere speck of formalin."

What Smith did was to telephone a man he did not know, then the prime minister of South Africa, Dr. Daniel F. Malan. Smith did not know it, but Dr. Malan's wife had obtained a copy of Smith's book *Sea Fishes of Southern Africa,* for Dr. Malan to read.

"They fetched him the book," Smith recalls, "and found the coelacanth pages in it. He read it over slowly and paged through part of the volume. Then he shut it. He called [his wife] again, and, tapping the book, said, 'The man that wrote this book would not ask my help at a time like this unless it was desperately important. I must speak to him.' "

So Prime Minister Malan and Dr. Smith had a long-distance conversation; Smith talked 12 minutes without a break. The result: Malan provided a government DC-3 to transport Smith to the Comoro Islands. Smith flew there as fast as the DC-3 at 180 miles an hour could get him there. He rushed to Eric Hunt's ship.

> Hunt pointed to a large coffin-like box near the mast, and I knew it must be in there. They picked up the box and put it on the hatch-cover, just in front of me, a foot above the deck, and Hunt pulled away the lid. I saw a sea of cottonwool, the fish was covered with it. . . .
>
> They all stood staring at me, but I could not bring myself to touch it; and, after standing as if stricken, motioned to them to open it, when Hunt and a sailor jumped as if electrified and peeled away that enveloping white shroud.
>
> God, yes! It was true! I saw first the unmistakable tubercles on the large scales, then the bones of the head, the spiny fins. It was true! . . . It was a coelacanth all right. I knelt down on the deck so as to get a closer view, and as I caressed that fish I found tears splashing on my

hands and realized that I was weeping, and was quite without shame. Fourteen of the best years of my life had gone in this search and it was true; it was really true. It had come at last.

The 1952 coelacanth was a different species from the 1938 one. Smith named the 1952 catch *Malania anjouanae,* for the prime minister and the island near where the fish was caught.

There was no 14-year wait for specimen No. 3. It was also caught off Anjouan Island, in 660 feet of water, by Houmadi Hassani on September 24, 1953. Four feet long, it weighed 88 pounds, or 20 pounds less than Houmadi Hassani himself did, was brown with white spots, and after death turned blue. On January 29, 1954, No. 4 was taken near Grande Comoro, the principal one of the Comoro Islands; Nos. 5 and 6 came up soon thereafter. No. 7 was caught later in 1954. So far all had been males. No. 8, September 12, 1954, was a female. By the middle 1960's, a total of 40 coelacanths had been caught. A preserved specimen has reached the American Museum of Natural History in New York City, where it will be studied for years. In 1965, the University of California at Los Angeles and the Los Angeles County Museum of Natural History each had a specimen; in May, 1966, Yale received one—frozen. There are, at the present time, no live coelacanths in captivity.

Jacques-Yves Cousteau went out in his ship *Calypso* to photograph the underwater haunts of the coelacanth near the Comoros. The inhabitants, he discovered, now call it *le poisson*, the fish.

A reward amounting to $560 had been offered by Professor James Millot of the Paris Museum of Natural History for a living specimen. Cousteau writes:

> One night two fishermen, Zema ben Said Mohamed and Madi Bacari, were sitting in their pirogue a mile offshore with catfish baits hanging 840 feet below. The moon came up and they felt a violent strike—from *le poisson* (the fish), Zema believed.

He and his partner decided to try for the $560 Millot had offered for a fish brought in alive.

> The two men strained to bring the fish to the surface. It was 5 feet long, and it was a coelacanth. They hauled the fighting giant alongside the pirogue, and Zema ran his hand along the line into the fish's mouth. His hook was lodged firmly in the palate. He thought they needed more control, so he reached into the mouth again and passed another line through the gill slit. With the coelacanth close-reined, Zema and Madi took up their paddles—wooded disks lashed to staves—and dug hard to bring the thrashing captive ashore. As often as not, the fish towed the slender boat.
>
> The little fishermen won. On the beach they placed the live fish in a whale boat full of water, and the populace got out of bed and danced and sang all night around *le poisson.* They stretched a net over the boat, but the coelacanth seemed to accept captivity. It swam slowly by rotating movements of its pectoral fins, using the second dorsal and anal fins as a rudder. The people lined the gunwales of the boat, looking in with awe at the glowing greenish-yellow eyes that seemed to cast light rather than reflect it.
>
> When the sun came up, the fish huddled in the darkest parts of the whale boat. It seemed physically hurt by light, so the villagers put a tent over the boat. Professor Millot arrived at noon, entered the tent, and stared in rapture at his first living coelacanth. It was losing strength and was swimming with increasing feebleness. In the midafternoon "the fish" rolled on its back, vibrated its fins convulsively, and died. Millot sadly concluded that it had been killed by photophobia, or sensitivity to light, perhaps with the drastic changes of temperature as a contributing cause. He paid Zema and Madi the double reward, and two more wealthy fishermen joined the local coelacanth aristocracy.

The coelacanth is, all by itself, a storehouse of many of the mysteries of the sea. It may also be a storehouse of some of the answers. The coelacanth, some scientists believe, is a relative of the extinct air-breathing rhipidistians, the aquatic ancestors of all land animals.

What is the composition of the prehistoric coelacanth's flesh? What are its amino acids? What is the nature of its cells? Does it have a liver? What kind of digestive juices? Those fins—did they become arms, and, if so, how? The coelacanth drips oil. It may help men tell if fish oil was part of the origin of petroleum on land and beneath the sea.

Writes Professor Smith,

> There is hardly a limit to what we may learn through the coelacanth. Almost all the creatures that lived 70 million years ago, both of the land and the sea, have vanished, and most of them would look strange or startling if they appeared now. Most people have heard of the dinosaurs and other giant reptiles, the enormous fish-eating lizards and flying reptiles, and other similar creatures of past ages. It requires little imagination to picture the sensation that would be caused if one of those gigantic dinosaurs ambled into civilization today. Indeed, the appearance of any piece of that long-buried past is an event. While the coelacanth is not the size of a dinosaur, its appearance, still alive, is in many ways much more startling.

CHAPTER
26

Some Unsolved Problems

"IN THE DEPTHS of the sea," said A. Hyatt Verrill, many years ago, "lie the greatest of the ocean's mysteries." Today the depths contain many unsolved problems that oceanographers are working on.

Where can more fish for food be found? In the South Atlantic "a billion dollars' worth of meat"—a new fishing ground—was recently discovered. Many tuna fishing boats, accordingly, are heading to the South Atlantic from the Pacific Coast. Near the Bahamas, the Bureau of Commercial Fisheries vessel *Geronimo* in 1966 sighted one of the biggest schools of bluefin tuna ever. For over two and one half hours the ship cruised through the school of thousands of 200- to 600-pound tuna. The sighting was at night. "It is impossible to estimate the size of this school," Paul N. Sund, who was along on the *Geronimo,* writes me. "The fish apparently were semidormant in the water and when disturbed by the approach of the boat would move rapidly and cause the water to flash. All hands enjoyed the show—not unlike a July 4th display." At Texas A. & M. University, Professor W. W. Meinke and his staff are working on a way to turn trash fish—the fish fishermen throw back, like hake, dogfish, rays and sea robins—into feed for animals and food for humans. Sometimes trash fish are nine-tenths of the fish in a trawl. A meal made from trash fish may be the eventual answer.

In 1964, assisted by the teeming fish in the Humboldt Current,

(Chapter 22), Peru caught twenty billion pounds of fish to lead the nations of the world. Peru was followed by Japan, Communist China, Russia, and the United States. A big part of Peru's catch: the silvery, 3-to-6-inch-long anchovetas, which Yale's Dan Merriman found blanketing the sea's surface in the Humboldt Current.

The sea creature that puts more money than any other in the pockets of U.S. fishermen is a small bewhiskered crustacean whose only edible part is its tail: the shrimp. It passed salmon and tuna in recent years. Shrimp fisheries extend all the way around from Cape Hatteras, North Carolina, to Port Isabel, Texas. There is a northern shrimp being taken off New England. A new fine-tasting royal red shrimp, lobster-red on your dining table, was discovered recently by the research vessel *Oregon* 1,000 to 1,500 feet down in the Gulf of Mexico. The shrimp industry began when a fisheries biologist off Beaufort, North Carolina, one summer morning in 1915 found shrimp in quantity in offshore coastal waters. From then on, U.S. shrimp fisheries grew. In the future fish may be raised as food crops, as beef cattle are now, and harvested with due care to the next generation. In that case Athelstan Spilhaus, the chairman of the Committee on Oceanography of the National Academy of Sciences-National Research Council and dean of the Institute of Technology at the University of Minnesota, writes in the *Bulletin of the Atomic Scientists* we might "steadily take from five to perhaps a hundred times the present amount out of the sea."

What else can we obtain from the sea? J. H. Clotworthy, vice president, Westinghouse Underseas Division, Baltimore, sums up: "There is abundant wealth in the sea." A few intriguing possibilities: From plants or from invertebrates we may obtain medicines, including antibiotics, insecticides, herbicides, soil conditioners, and fertilizers. Seaweed provides iodine; it also provides a jellylike byproduct that, when scattered from a low-flying airplane, can fireproof grass and brush. Seaweed is eaten in Japan and elsewhere.

Do the continents move? Because of their shapes, especially the coasts of South America and Africa, it has been suggested that the continents might once have been joined together, like pieces of a jigsaw puzzle. One theory has been that Africa, South America, Antarctica, India, and other Southern Hemisphere land once formed a single continent, called Gondwana land, which split apart and then separated by a slow drifting action over many millennia. Now scientists are trying to check the ages of rocks on the Brazilian and South African coasts. If the ages of the rocks match, the theory of continental drift, points out Dr. John Reynolds of the University of California, will be greatly strengthened.

How can we explain the strip of Pacific Ocean, from Panama to Baja California, Mexico, where fish grow to be monsters? Here normally 20-pound yellowtails grow to over 100 pounds in weight. Here 250-pound marlin turn into 2,500-pound giants. Here sea plants grow three-foot-thick trunks like trees and grow several hundred feet long. Fish in the strip seem to be immune to disease. The water is free of poisonous bacteria or parasites. The water may even contain some special medical ingredient that man could use.

What causes tsunamis—the dreaded tidal waves that race over the sea and deluge coastal areas? A. W. Anderson, an oceanographer assistant in the U.S. Coast and Geodetic Survey's office of oceanography, writes me that the causes could be earthquakes, or volcanic alterations of the ocean floor, or submarine avalanches on the slopes of Pacific trenches, or all of these.

How do the green turtles navigate? By tagging green turtles, Professor Archie Carr of the University of Florida and Harold Hirth, one of Carr's graduate students, have discovered something simply astounding: Some green turtles cross 1,400 miles of the Atlantic from Brazil and manage to find unfailingly tiny (5-mile-long) Ascension Island, where they lay eggs. Since the 300- to 500-pound turtle swims on or below the surface, this appears more astonishing than the migration of birds—a bird, from its height, can use its eyes better to find its way. To learn how the great turtles do it, Carr wants to put tiny radio sets on them, have the sets broadcast their positions to satellites, and so learn what route the turtles follow.

Is a flying submarine possible, or is it a pipedream? You may have read, from time to time, of talk about an airplane that could land on the sea and become a submarine. The U.S. Navy has a flying submarine on the drawing board. It would be a seaplane with three jet engines. After it landed on the sea, it would flood (all of it, except for the pilot's compartment, and the battery and instrument sections), and the flooding would take the plane down to depths of 150 to 200 feet. In the air, the flying submarine would fly at 300 knots. Beneath the sea, the flying submarine would cruise at up to 10 knots.

What new weapons for use in the depths will improve our defenses? The question continually requires new answers. In the winter of 1965–66, Aerojet-General Corporation was producing our first underwater guided missile, powered by a solid-fuel rocket motor. This is the Mark 46-0 torpedo, not really a torpedo at all. It is a missile that ranges deeper and farther than any previous antisubmarine weapon. With its electronic equipment it searches for submarines, and homes in when it finds one. It can be launched by destroyers, frigates, drone helicopters (no human pilot on board), and long-range aircraft—but not by our submarines. Captain Grady H. Lowe, officer-in-charge, Naval Ordnance Test Station, Pasadena, California, says the Navy has been waiting for a long time for a weapon like the Mark 46-0.

Another new antisubmarine weapon is Subroc. This one is used by our submarines, including the new nuclear antisubmarine submarine *Dace*. In the Subroc system, a torpedo is fired that can travel underwater, rise into the air, drop its rocket booster, follow a trajectory, and reenter the sea to chase an enemy submarine. *Dace* herself is a new kind of weapon for the depths. One of eight new nuclear submarines built by Ingalls Shipbuilding Division of Litton Industries at Pascagoula, Mississippi, she has 1,000 hydrophones in her bow and along her sides and is probably the world's champion listener. She can run silently and listen and pick up sounds of enemy submarines as no other submarine can. "Our function," her captain has said, "is stealth."

One new nuclear carrier—expected to need refueling only once in her 25-year life—was approved for the Navy in 1966. Two more were tentatively scheduled for future years. The Navy's Deep Submergence program, which in 1966 changed its name to PM (for Project Management) 11, will eventually, says *Ocean Science News,* take the operational Navy into the really deep ocean. This means in the long run developing a deep-sea combat fleet. Northrop's Nortronics Division is the prime management and engineering support contractor for PM 11.

What else can be expected from the Office of Naval Research and all the Navy's ships and stations and laboratories working on oceanography? "The Navy," says Vice Admiral Lawson P. Ramage, deputy chief of naval operations, "is going to open up all the oceans."

What animal makes what sound? To help sonar and sound operators, Robert L. Eberhardt of the Lockheed-California Company has been studying the sounds made by sea creatures and the echoes they return to sound apparatus. A surprising thing that Eberhardt told me was that all whales may not return an echo. Something about the bone surface under the blubber, in the case of some whales, seems to dissipate the echo.

What is the geological history of the earth? How has it affected man? The answers to these questions are sought by Maurice Ewing and his associates at the Lamont Geological Observatory of Columbia University. They seek the answers in the sediments on the sea floor. From Columbia University's *Vema* and other ships, Ewing's men have obtained over 4,000 cores of sediment, more than anyone else. They have figured out that sediment accumulates at, very roughly, an inch in a thousand years. They have learned to distinguish between the remains in the sediment of microscopic warm and cold water animals. From all this they have figured out a new time span for the Pleistocene Epoch—1½ million years, far longer than had been thought. The Pleistocene (or "most recent") geological epoch, which continues today, they believe, has been punctuated by four ice ages. This is the long epoch in which man as he exists today developed.

Can we actually expect to find more unknown animals in the sea? Yes. Like the coelacanth and the University of Miami's fish that hauls its own trawl, they keep being discovered. One of the last places you would look for unknown animals is Georges Bank. This bank has been fished so much and so long you would not believe an unknown specimen could be found there. Yet the Woods Hole dragger *Cap'n Bill III,* owned by Henry W. Klimm, Jr., hauled up from about 2,340 feet down, on Georges Bank, three strange fish. Dr. Richard H. Backus was along researching the deep scattering layer. Dr. Daniel M. Cohen of the U.S. Fish and Wildlife Service concluded the three fish were a previously unknown genus of the cusk eel. The strange fish are unusual indeed— they are without scales.

Will we ever capture a giant squid? Woods Hole scientists had a near miss not long ago. When they hauled up a trawl they found that a giant squid had left part of a big tentacle, or arm, entangled in one of their lines. And when a 34-foot-long female sperm whale was stranded 90 miles north of Miami recently, Bill Stephens found what the squid had done to her: circular scars from the squid's suckers. "On the whale's head," he said, "we found scars made by the suckers and claws of giant squids. Some of the circular sucker marks were one and a quarter inches in diameter. This would indicate that the whale had tangled with a squid of enormous proportions."

What can be learned about other strange newly discovered animals? A startling recent discovery—this one from one of the deepest points in the sea—was made by the Russians. They hauled up from the Kurile-Kamchatka Trench threadlike, wormlike animals up to 5 feet long called pogonophores. They live in tubes that each animal makes for itself, and they are so unlike other animals that they have been placed in their own phylum. Pogonophores have a brain but no breathing organs, no sense organs, no mouth, no digestive system. They are believed to eat by absorbing food particles from the sea. Dr. Libbie Hyman, a biologist at the American Museum of Natural History, says the finding of the pogonophore ranks in importance with the discovery of the coelacanth and of neopilina, the ancient snail-like creature (Chapter 20).

On October 1, 1965, *Science,* the magazine of the American Association for the Advancement of Science, reported that a Columbia University oceanographer, Bruce C. Heezen, together with Donald W. Bourne of the University of Cambridge, England, had lowered a camera to the bottom of the Pacific and made a photo 15,534 feet (or nearly three miles) deep that solved a mystery. It showed the animal that makes previously unexplained coiled, or spiral, tracks on the bottom of the sea. The tracks had been found by the *Eltanin,* a Navy Antarctic research ship and by many other vessels in dozens of deep-sea-floor photos. But the maker of the tracks had not been identified. It was an acorn worm, a rare creature. The Columbia-Cambridge picture shows the worm actually making the tracks. The acorn worm became known to man when the *Challenger* dredged up the first three specimens of it in the 1870's.

How can robots help in the depths? A robot, built by the Hughes Aircraft Company and designed by the Shell Oil Company, has appeared 1,000 feet down on the sea floor. Dick Nelson of Shell told me about him. One of his names is Mobot. Another is the UNUMO[R] robot. You can see a model of Mobot in the Hall of Petroleum at the Smithsonian Institution's Museum of History and Technology in Washington, D.C. Mobot locates oil wellheads and closes valves and tightens bolts as necessary. By means of his TV camera eye Mobot recently sighted a sea serpent, a 15-foot-long ribbon of small marine organisms.

A robot that operates even deeper, to 2,000 feet, is CURV of the Naval Ordnance Test Station, Pasadena, California. CURV, says Dr. William G. McLean, technical director of NOTS, can find and bring to the surface torpedoes from 2,000 feet down. CURV brought up the H-bomb we lost in the Mediterranean.

What can a robot submarine do? N. J. (Nick) Delaney described to me Lear Siegler, Inc.'s Sonodiver. It's almost a submarine. Small and unmanned, it can carry scientific instruments nearly four miles down and return on its own.

How useful will unmanned weather stations prove? The United States late in 1965 had the first eight unmanned weather floats in operation around the seas. They broadcast automatically wind, waves, temperatures, and barometric conditions. One, operated by Texas A. & M. University, had saved lives when it predicted a hurricane. University of Washington oceanography students, having discovered their own undersea mountain, or seamount, are erecting upon it a system to collect and broadcast automatically weather and oceanographic information.

Will we ever end seasickness? This would greatly help sailors, oceanographers, and all who sail upon the sea. As a preliminary step, the Boeing Company has built a ship-motion simulator—a weird framework that simulates the heave and roll of the ocean. It tests the effects of the sea's movements upon those who ride it. *Some* volunteers say they enjoy it. The world's biggest shipping line, the P. & O. (the Peninsular and Oriental Steam Navigation Company, Ltd.) operates the *Canberra,* a theoretically seasick-proof passenger liner. She has Denny-Brown stabilizers and a bulbous bow to reduce her motions, and her engines are at the stern —not amidship—to reduce vibration.

Can we equip all ships to navigate by satellites? Navy ships and the Coast and Geodetic Survey ocean survey vessel *Pioneer* have been testing a prototype set to receive information from the Transit satellite. The *Pioneer*'s receiver feeds information received into a computer, which uses it, together with other information, to compute a ship's position. The problem: to bring down the cost and size of the receiver and computer so that they may be used by commercial ships, fishermen, and pleasure boats.

Can we learn more about those great undersea waves? More may be learned about the waves (like those located by the Coast and Geodetic Survey, Chapter 10) by men aboard *Flip,* a Navy ship that can be made to stand straight up lengthwise in the ocean. *Flip,* 355 feet long, is full of scientific instruments. She looks like a big log floating in the sea. She is towed to a position for research, then the water is let into one end and that end sinks. *Flip* stands up in the ocean—55 feet of her, containing quarters for 5 scientists and 7 crew members, remains above the surface. *Flip* is a stable platform, moving only a few inches in a heavy sea. She is to do acoustical studies, including research on the internal waves, in the Pacific 200 miles off Maui, Hawaii. The United States has one other research vessel, *Spar,* that stands up in the sea the same way; *Spar* is unmanned.

Why does a shark's heart stand still? Dr. Warren J. Wisby, a contractor for the Office of Naval Research, implanted electrodes in sharks and recorded their heartbeats by means of electrocardiographs. He discovered, amazingly enough, that the heart of the lemon shark stops beating when it suffers an electric shock, when it is frightened, or when it is chasing prey. "This curious behavior —the cessation of heart action at precisely the time when tissue demands for oxygen and nutrients are greatest—is as yet not understood," says *Naval Research Reviews.*

Will we breathe the sea? With man about to drink the sea, by separating the fresh water from the salt in it, he may also be about to breathe the sea, by separating the oxygen from the liquid in it. Waldemar (Wally) Ayres, a New Jersey man, on two occasions has inhaled the sea, both times for longer than an hour. On the first time, a demonstration that lasted 90 minutes on August 6, 1962, at Jones Beach, New York, he became the first man in history to breathe the sea. He repeated the feat later. Ayres breathes oxygen from seawater by means of a watertight membrane he invented. The liquid is held back by the membrane but oxygen, dissolved in the water, comes on through the membrane —and can be inhaled. Further, carbon dioxide, which men breathe out, passes the other way through the membrane and is thus got rid of.

Ayres's membrane thus works like the gill of a fish. A fish's gill contains thin membranes through which oxygen dissolved in the water is absorbed by the fish and through which the fish's waste products are given off. Ayres's apparatus at present is cumbersome. He is reducing its size so that a diver will be able to carry it. The Patent Office in January 1966 issued Ayres a patent.

Walter Robb, a General Electric scientist, also has developed a film, a fine silicone, that similarly acts as a sieve or filter to obtain oxygen from seawater, and that passes carbon dioxide the other way. Robb has kept animals—hamsters and rabbits— underwater in a goldfish bowl for up to four days, breathing through his film. Each animal was in a box with top and two sides of Robb's film. The animals were unharmed when he ended his experiments with them.

Submarines as well as divers may one day obtain life-giving oxygen right out of the ocean by means of filtering the water through film. To get breathable oxygen from the water instead of being drowned by the sea would change man's entire relation to the sea. And it would give him all the time in the world to remain below the surface and explore the depths. "We need to put men on the ocean bottom as free agents," Astronaut-Aquanaut Scott Carpenter not long ago said at Texas A. & M. University. To breathe oxygen from the water would help immeasurably.

What did the search for the H-bomb reveal? Early in 1966, the Navy's Task Force 65, Rear Admiral William S. Guest commanding, took up the search for a 12-by-2-foot H-bomb on the bottom of the Mediterranean Sea. The H-bomb—which was not armed and not about to explode—had been accidentally dropped in a crash of U.S. Air Force planes over Spain. The deep-diving vehicles

Alvin (Chapter 2), *Aluminaut* (Chapter 8), and *Deep Jeep* (Chapter 2), were flown or shipped to the scene. A *Cubmarine* (Chapter 4) and Jon Lindbergh (Chapter 3) joined the search. Over half a mile down, *Alvin* (her pilots, alternating, were Bill Rainnie, Marvin J. McCamis, and Valentine Wilson) found the H-bomb—an incredible feat in murky water where visibility *with* floodlights was 30 feet. *Alvin* and *Aluminaut* took turns guarding the bomb lest it slip away for good into sea-bottom ooze. The robot CURV rammed two grappling hooks into the risers of a parachute still attached to the bomb. U.S.S. *Petrel* hoisted the bomb to her deck. There was now no chance a U.S. H-bomb would fall into enemy hands.

The search for the H-bomb was the biggest deep-sea search-and-recovery ever attempted in all history. Nothing like it had been done—or even contemplated—before. The new U.S. deep-diving craft made it possible. Eyewitnesses over half a mile down found the bomb. Eyewitnesses guarded it till it could be retrieved. The H-bomb recovery, a national triumph for the United States, showed spectacularly that science has given man a new ability: to explore the depths.

What has the sea meant to us, and what can it mean in the years ahead? Ships, like the *Mayflower* (which reached Plymouth, Massachusetts, in 1620) or the *Goodspeed, Sarah Constant,* and *Discovery* (which reached Virginia in 1607), have meant for our ancestors the start of a new life in a new world—a world discovered and opened up by voyaging. Whale oil from the sea lighted our lamps till kerosene replaced it just a century ago. Whale oil was better than candles; it enabled people better to read and study extensively after dark and so helped further education and the pursuit of science and literature. To many of us, the sea is summed up in the Bible: "In the beginning God created the heaven and the earth. And the earth was without form, and void; and darkness was upon the face of the deep. And the Spirit of God moved upon the face of the waters" (Gen. 1:1-2).

The sea is the Breton fishermen's prayer: "The sea is so wide, and my boat is so small." The sea is prose by Joseph Conrad and Herman Melville and H. M. Tomlinson, and poetry by John Masefield.

The sea to many of us is a picture like *The Breakers* by Frederick J. Waugh, or a painting by Winslow Homer, or one of the great Dutch seascapes, or a print by Currier and Ives. The sea is "Anchors Aweigh" or Debussy's *La Mer*. It is a clipper ship like Britain's *Cutty Sark* or America's *Flying Cloud*. The clippers learned to turn the hazardous winds of the Roaring Forties into helpful assistance, and so, as men exploring the depths will do, they turned danger into advantage.

The sea is the North Star and the Southern Cross and the rush you hear when you hold a shell to your ear. The sea is journey's end. It is the Verrazano-Narrows Bridge across the Narrows, the mile-wide entrance to New York Harbor. It is San Francisco's Golden Gate Bridge. It marks the boundaries of the United States: ". . . From sea to shining sea." The sea is the America's Cup yacht races, an ancient map by Mercator or Ortelius, a trip on a ferryboat, a scrimshaw carving on ivory whale teeth. It is the Gloucester fisherman. The sea is Lepanto, Trafalgar, Jutland, Dunkirk. The sea is the 44-gun U.S.S. *Constitution* vs. the *Guerriere,* Pearl Harbor, Midway, Iwo Jima. The sea reaches "from the halls of Montezuma to the shores of Tripoli." The sea is John Paul Jones.

The sea is Nathaniel Bowditch and *The New American Practical Navigator,* first published in 1802. The sea is the Virginian, Lieutenant Matthew Fontaine Maury, U.S. Navy, who issued his first wind and current charts of the Atlantic in the middle 1800's, and it is all the oceanographers who have followed Maury. A few are: Henry Bryant Bigelow, first director of Woods Hole; Columbus O'Donnell Iselin, investigator of the Gulf Stream, director of Woods Hole from 1940 to 1950, a scientist who during World War II predicted what type of surf would strike any beach at any time; and Francis Parker Shepard, teaching the geology of the sea to a generation of students at Scripps. The sea was Maurice Ewing, the Rice Institute college freshman in 1922, gazing at the sea for the first time in his life from the seawall at Galveston, Texas, and thinking the waves were awful big. It is Maurice Ewing today, of whose associates, in Columbia University's Lamont Geological Observatory, Britain's Royal Geographical Society says: "There are no oceans where Lamont scientists have not been working."

Travel by sea has given us the world we know. Columbus. Vasco da Gama. Ponce de Leon. Balboa. Cortes. Tristan da Cunha. Amerigo Vespucci. Cartier. De Soto. Coronado. Raleigh. Hudson. Cook. Magellan. Humboldt. Darwin in H.M.S. *Beagle*. Amundsen. Shackleton. Scott. Byrd.

Many of us remember the sea from our World War II service: a trip aboard the *West Point* or the *Queen Elizabeth;* serving in a naval vessel; or the beating we got on an amphibious-force landing craft. The sea is a Coast Guard weather ship holding station on the winter North Atlantic, or the sea is a luxury cruise to the warm Caribbean, with calm seas and moonlit nights and romance. Quiet or stormy, cloudy or starry, the oceans are beside us all the time and we use them. Our past was linked to the sea. Our present is linked to the sea. Our future? It depends on what men find in the depths, on what eyewitnesses discover beneath the waves. "The great unknown," said Peter Freuchen, "now lies beneath the surface of the waters."

Bibliography

BOOKS

Allee, W. C., and Schmidt, Karl P., *Ecological Animal Geography*. John Wiley & Sons, Inc., New York, 1951.
Contains much on sea creatures.

Anderson, William R. (Commander, U.S.N.), *"Nautilus" 90 North*. The World Publishing Company, New York, 1959.
Voyage of first nuclear submarine to North Pole.

Armstrong, E. F., and Miall, L. M., *Raw Materials from the Sea*. Chemical Publishing Co., Inc., New York, 1946.

Arnov, Boris, Jr., *Oceans of the World*. The Bobbs-Merrill Company, Inc., Indianapolis, 1962.

Bascom, Willard, *The Hole in the Bottom of the Sea*. Doubleday & Company, Inc., Garden City, N.Y., 1961.
Mohole project.

Beach, Edward L. (Captain, U.S.N.), *Around the World Submerged: The Voyage of the "Triton."* Holt, Rinehart and Winston, New York, 1962.

Beebe, William, *Beneath Tropic Seas*. G. P. Putnam's Sons, New York, 1928.

———— *Half Mile Down*. Duell, Sloan and Pearce, New York, 1934 and 1951.

———— *Zaca Venture*. Harcourt, Brace and Company, New York, 1938.

Berrill, N. J., *The Living Tide*. Fawcett Publications, Inc., New York, 1956.

———— *1001 Questions about the Seashore*. Dodd, Mead & Company, New York, 1957.

Bixby, William, *Track of the "Bear"* (1873–1963). David McKay Company, Inc., New York, 1965.

Bear was a famous Arctic cutter for the Coast Guard.

Borgstrom, G., *Japan's World Success in Fishing.* Fishing News Ltd., London.

Breland, Osmond P., *Animal Life and Lore.* Harper & Row, New York, 1963.

Dr. Breland keeps careful records of all kinds of wild animals—including marine animals.

Bruun, Anton Frederic; Greve, Svend Bernhard; Mielche, Hakon; and Sparck, Hakon Ragnar G., *The Galathea Deep Sea Expedition, 1950–1952,* trans. by Reginald Spink. Allen and Unwin, London, 1956.

Burton, Maurice, *Margins of the Sea.* Harper & Brothers, New York, 1954.

Caidin, Martin, *Hydrospace.* E. P. Dutton & Co., Inc., New York, 1964.

Calvert, James (Commander, U.S.N.), *Surface at the Pole.* McGraw-Hill Book Co., Inc., New York, 1960.

Trips to North Pole of nuclear submarine *Skate.*

Carrington, Richard, *A Biography of the Sea.* Basic Books, Inc., New York, 1960.

Carson, Rachel L., *The Edge of the Sea.* Houghton Mifflin Company; soft-cover edition by Mentor Books, New York, 1941.

———— *The Sea Around Us.* Oxford University Press; soft-cover edition by Mentor Books, New York, 1950.

———— *Under the Sea Wind.* Oxford University Press; soft-cover edition by Mentor Books, New York, 1955.

Challenger Reports. Reprints available from Johnson Reprint Corporation, New York, N.Y.

Fifty volumes on the 1872–76 voyage that founded oceanography: animals, minerals, depths, salinity, etc.

Chapin, Henry, and Smith, F. G. Walton, *The Ocean River.* Charles Scribner's Sons, New York, 1952.

Chapman, Sydney, *I G Y: Year of Discovery.* University of Michigan Press, Ann Arbor, 1959.

Clarke, Arthur C., and Wilson, Mike, *The Treasure of the Great Reef.* Harper & Row, New York, 1964.

Colman, John S., *The Sea and Its Mysteries*. W. W. Norton & Company, Inc., New York, 1950.

Constance, Arthur, *The Impenetrable Sea*. The Citadel Press, New York, 1958.

Cousteau, Jacques-Yves, *The Silent World*. Harper & Row; soft-cover edition Pocket Books Inc., New York, 1953.

———— with Dugan, James, *The Living Sea*. Harper & Row, New York, 1963.

———— *World Without Sun*. Harper & Row, New York, 1965.
Cousteau's first colony of men living beneath the sea.

Cowen, Robert C., *Frontiers of the Sea*. Doubleday & Company, Inc., New York, 1960.

Cromie, William J., *Exploring the Secrets of the Sea*. Prentice-Hall, Inc., Englewood Cliffs, N.J., 1962.

Crompton, John, *The Living Sea*. Doubleday & Company, Inc., New York, 1957.

Deacon, G. E. R., ed., *Seas, Maps, and Men*. Doubleday & Company, Inc., New York, 1962.

Diolé, Philippe, *4000 Years Under the Sea*. Julian Messner, Inc., New York, 1954.

Dugan, James, and Vahan, Richard, *Men Under Water*. Chilton Books, Philadelphia and New York, 1965.
An anthology for the Underwater Society of America.

Dunbar, M. J., ed., *Marine Distributions*. University of Toronto Press, in cooperation with The Royal Society of Canada, 1963.

Engel, Leonard, and the Editors of Life, *The Sea*. Time Inc., New York, 1961.

Ericson, David B., and Wollin, Goesta, *The Deep and the Past*. Alfred A. Knopf, New York, 1964.
Tells how Columbia University men, under Maurice Ewing, traced the time span known as the Pleistocene in the sediments on the deep-sea floor.

Fraser, James, *Nature Adrift*. Dufour Editions, Philadelphia, 1962.

Freuchen, Peter, with Loth, David, *Peter Freuchen's Book of the Seven Seas*. Julian Messner, Inc., New York, 1957.

Gaskell, T. F., *Under the Deep Oceans*. W. W. Norton & Company, Inc., New York, 1960.
Geology; finding of the Challenger Deep.

Gaul, Albro, *The Wonderful World of the Seashore*. Appleton-Century-Crofts, Inc., New York, 1955.

Gray, William B., *Creatures of the Sea*. Wilfred Funk, Inc., New York, 1960.

―――― *Porpoise Tales*. A. S. Barnes and Co., New York, 1964.

Günther, Klaus, and Deckert, Kurt, *Creatures of the Deep Sea*. Charles Scribner's Sons, New York, 1956.

Hardy, Alister, *The Open Sea*. Houghton Mifflin Company, Boston, 1956.
The plankton.

Hegner, Robert W., and Stiles, Karl A., *College Zoology*, 6th ed. The Macmillan Company, New York, 1951.

Hill, M. N., ed., *The Sea*. John Wiley & Sons, Inc., New York; Vol. 1, 1962; Vol. 2, 1963; Vol. 3, 1963.
Brings up to date the story of oceanography, physics and chemistry of the sea, the sea floor, origin of life in the sea.

Houot, Georges, and Willm, Pierre, *2000 Fathoms Down*. E. P. Dutton & Co., Inc., New York, 1955.
Bathyscaphe diving.

Idyll, C. P., *Abyss: The Deep Sea and the Creatures That Live in It*. Thomas Y. Crowell Company, New York, 1964.

King, C. A. M., *Introduction to Oceanography*. McGraw-Hill Book Co., Inc., 1963.

Landrin, Armand, *The Monsters of the Deep*. T. Nelson and Sons, London, 1875.

Lane, Frank W., *Kingdom of the Octopus*. Jarrolds, London, 1957.

Leif, Hans, *The River in the Sea*. G. P. Putnam's Sons, New York, 1958.

Life (magazine), *A Guide to the Natural World*. Time Inc., New York, 1965.

Long, E. John, *New World of Oceanography*. Pyramid Publications, Inc., New York, 1965 (a paperback).

Lonsdale, A. L., and Kaplan, H. R., *Guide to Sunken Ships in American Waters*. Compass Publications, Inc., Arlington, Va., 1964.

McClane, A. J., *McClane's Standard Fishing Encyclopedia and International Angling Guide*. Holt, Rinehart & Winston, New York, 1965.

McCormick, Harold W., Allen, Tom, and Young, William, *Shadows in the Sea*. Chilton Co., Book Division, Philadelphia, Pa., 1963.

Menard, H. W., *Marine Geology of the Pacific*. McGraw-Hill Book Co., Inc., New York, 1964.

Mero, John L., *The Mineral Resources of the Sea*. American Elsevier Publishing Co., Inc., New York, 1964.

Murray, Sir John, *The Ocean*. Henry Holt and Company, New York, undated.

—— and Hjort, Johan, *The Depths of the Ocean*. Macmillan and Co., Ltd., London, 1912.

Ommanney, F. D., *A Draught of Fishes*. Longmans Green and Co. Ltd., London, 1965.

Ommanney, F. D., and the Editors of Life, *The Fishes*. Time Inc., New York, 1963.

Phillips, Craig, *The Captive Sea*. Chilton Co., Book Division, Philadelphia, Pa., 1964.
Aquariums—especially Miami Seaquarium.

Piccard, Jacques, and Dietz, Robert S., *Seven Miles Down*. G. P. Putnam's Sons, New York, 1961.
The deepest dive so far made by men, in the bathyscaphe *Trieste*.

Polmar, Norman, *Death of the "Thresher."* Chilton Co., Book Division, Philadelphia, Pa., 1964.

Ritchie, George Stephen, *"Challenger": The Life of a Survey Ship*. Abelard-Schuman Ltd., New York, 1958.

Roberts, Fred, *Basic Scuba*. D. Van Nostrand Co., Inc., Princeton, N.J., 1960.

Schultz, Leonard P., and others, *Wondrous World of Fishes*. National Geographic Society, Washington, D.C., 1965.
Angling; freshwater, saltwater, and tropical fish; even recipes.

Sears, Mary, ed., *Progress in Oceanography*. The Macmillan Company, New York, 1964.

Smith, J. L. B., *The Search Beneath the Sea*. Henry Holt, New York, 1956.
   The first-person story of the discovery of the prehistoric coelacanth —alive—by its discoverer.

Stenuit, Robert, *The Deepest Days*. Coward-McCann, Inc., New York, 1966.

Stephens, William M., *Science Beneath the Sea*. G. P. Putnam's Sons, New York, 1966.

Sverdrup, H. U., Johnson, Martin W., and Fleming, Richard H., *The Oceans*. Prentice-Hall, Inc., Englewood Cliffs, N.J., 1942.

Tailliez, Philippe, *To Hidden Depths*. E. P. Dutton & Co., Inc., New York, 1954.

Thomson, Philip D., O'Brien, Robert, and the Editors of Life, *Weather*. Time Inc., New York, 1965.

Troebst, Cord-Christian, *Conquest of the Sea*. Harper & Row, New York, 1962.

Verrill, A. Hyatt, *The Ocean and Its Mysteries*. Duffield & Co., New York, 1916.

———— *Strange Creatures of the Sea*. Grosset & Dunlap, New York, 1955.

———— *The Strange Story of Our Earth*. Grosset & Dunlap, New York, 1952.

Villiers, Alan, *Men, Ships, and the Sea*. National Geographic Society, Washington, D.C., 1963.

Walford, Lionel A., *Living Resources of the Sea*. The Ronald Press Company, New York, 1958.

PERIODICALS; MAGAZINE AND NEWSPAPER ARTICLES

Baldwin, Hanson W., "New Submarines Will Explore the Last Frontier." *New York Times*, July 26, 1965.

———— "Undersea Research and Exploration Growing Rapidly Throughout the World." *New York Times*, July 25, 1965.

"Chemistry and the Oceans." *Chemical & Engineering News*, Washington, D.C., The American Chemical Society, Vol. 42, No. 22, June 1, 1964.

Cleary, John, "Oceans Still Unexploited While Man Tests Space." *Hartford* (Conn.) *Times*, March 25, 1965.

"Conquest of the Seas Called as Valuable as Moon Venture." *New York World-Telegram & Sun,* December 3, 1965.
Quotes Wilbert McLeod Chapman, oceanographer for Ralston-Purina Co., and Dr. Charles F. Jones, president of Humble Oil & Refining Co.

Duggan, Dennis, "Companies Hunt Untapped Riches Beneath the Sea." *New York Herald Tribune,* October 25, 1964.

Elia, Charles, "From Oil Rig to Trawler Fleet, Oceanics Explores New World." *New York World-Telegram & Sun,* June 6, 1964.

Engineering and Mining Journal. New York, McGraw-Hill Publications, May, June, July, August, 1965.

GeoMarine Technology. Washington, D.C., Intel, Inc.; ten times a year.

Heezen, Bruce C., "Whales Entangled in Deep Sea Cables." *Deep Sea Research, International Journal of Oceanography,* London, Vol. 4, pp. 105–115, 1957.

Industrial Research. Beverly Shores, Ind., Industrial Research, Inc.; monthly.

International Journal of Oceanology and Limnology. Haddonfield, N.J., Omnipress; starting in 1966.

International Marine Science. New York, UNESCO and FAO (Food and Agricultural Organization); quarterly.

Life: Special issues on the oceans. February 9, 1953; December 21, 1962.

Maritimes. Kingston, R.I., University of Rhode Island Graduate School of Oceanography; quarterly.
Official publication.

Missiles and Rockets: Special Report on Oceanology. Washington, D.C., American Aviation Publications, Inc., September 6, 1965.

National/Maine Coast Fisherman. Camden, Me., Russell W. Brace, publisher; monthly.
A tabloid-sized newspaper.

Naval Institute Proceedings. Annapolis, Md., U.S. Naval Institute; monthly.

Naval Research Reviews. Washington, D.C., Office of Naval Research; monthly.

Ocean Science News. Washington, D.C., Nautilus Press, Inc.; weekly.
Newsletter covering all of oceanography.

Oceanus. Woods Hole, Mass., The Woods Hole Oceanographic Institution; four times a year.

Sea Frontiers. Miami, Fla., International Oceanographic Foundation; six times a year.
Well illustrated; for the layman.

Sea Secrets. Miami, Fla., International Oceanographic Foundation; monthly.

"Search for Subs." *Space Aeronautics,* New York, Conover-Mast Publications, September, 1965.
The U.S. Navy and antisubmarine warfare.

Signal: Special oceanography issue. Washington, D.C., Armed Forces Communications and Electronics Association, October, 1965.

Soule, Gardner, "In Quest of the Key to Davy Jones' Locker." *Elks Magazine,* New York, Benevolent and Protective Order of Elks, August, 1965.

———— and Armagnac, Alden P., "The Fabulous Machines That Recovered Our H-Bomb." *Popular Science,* New York, June, 1966.

Spilhaus, Athelstan, "Oceanography: A Wet and Wondrous Journey." *Bulletin of the Atomic Scientists,* Chicago, Ill., Bulletin of the Atomic Scientists & Educational Foundation for Nuclear Science, Inc., December, 1964.

Tangerman, E. J., "The Deep Sea." *Product Engineering,* New York, McGraw-Hill Publications, March 14, 1966.

Trajectory. Sunnyvale, Calif., Lockheed Missiles & Space Company, Fall, 1964.

"Undersea Warfare." *Inquiry,* University Park, Pa., Pennsylvania State University, November, 1965.

Underwater Naturalist. Highlands, N.J., American Littoral Society, Sandy Hook Marine Laboratory.

Vine, Allyn, "Tools for Ocean Research," *International Science and Technology,* New York, Conover-Mast Publications, December, 1965; see also issue of March, 1965.

Willatt, Norris, "Wealth from the Sea? Venturesome Companies Are Taking the Plunge into Oceanography." *Barron's National Business & Financial Weekly,* Chicopee, Mass., Dow Jones & Co., Inc., May 17, 1965.

RECENT PUBLICATIONS OF SPECIAL INTEREST

Bibliography of Oceanographic Publications. Interagency Committee on Oceanography (ICO) of the Federal Council for Science and Technology; ICO Pamphlet No. 9, April, 1963.

Economic Benefits from Oceanographic Research. National Academy of Sciences-National Research Council; Publication 1228, 1964.

National Oceanographic Program Fiscal Year 1967. Interagency Committee on Oceanography (ICO) of the Federal Council for Science and Technology; ICO Pamphlet No. 24, March, 1966.

Ocean Sciences and National Security. Report of the Committee on Science and Astronautics, U.S. House of Representatives, 86th Congress, 2d Session; Union Calendar No. 920, House Report No. 2078, July 1, 1960.

Report of the Deep Submergence Systems Review Group. U.S. Navy, March 1, 1964.
Proposals for Navy's future deep-diving craft.

Sources of Information on Oceanography. National Academy of Sciences-National Research Council, Earth Sciences Division, Committee on Oceanography; November, 1965.
Lists oceanographic laboratories, institutions, private organizations, and government agencies.

Transactions. Marine Technology Society.
Papers presented at the Ocean Science and Ocean Engineering Conference and Exhibit at Washington, D.C., June 14–17, 1965.

University Curricula in Oceanography Academic Year 1965–66. Interagency Committee on Oceanography (ICO) of the Federal Council for Science and Technology; ICO Pamphlet No. 23, December, 1965.
Tells what universities concerned with oceanography are offering.

Vetter, Richard C., compiler, *An International Directory of Oceanographers.* National Academy of Sciences-National Research Council, Committee on Oceanography; 4th edition, 1964.

Index